CONSERVATION OF IRON

Edited by

R. W. CLARKE

Archaeological Research Centre
National Maritime Museum

and

S. M. BLACKSHAW

Department of Conservation and Technical Services
British Museum

This volume is the proceedings of a symposium held at the National Maritime Museum, Greenwich on July 4th 1980 which was jointly organised by the Archaeological Research Centre, National Maritime Museum and the Department of Convervation and Technical Services, British Museum.

Maritime Monographs and Reports

No. 53 – 1982

Published by the Trustees of the National Maritime Museum

ISBN 0307–8590
ISBN 0 905555 59 7

Printed in England by Yale Press Ltd. South Norwood SE25

'Gold is for the mistress – silver for the maid,
Copper for the craftsman cunning at his trade,
"Good!" said the Baron, sitting in his hall,
But iron, cold iron is master of them all.'

Rudyard Kipling "Cold Iron"

FOREWORD

In October 1973, the National Maritime Museum and the British Museum jointly organised a symposium to discuss problems in the conservation of waterlogged wood; the subsequent publication of the proceedings filled an important gap in the conservation literature (Maritime Monographs and Reports No. 16 – 1975, edited by W. A. Oddy). These two institutions again combined their expertise in 1980 in the organisation of a conference on the conservation of archaeological ironwork. As with the waterlogged wood symposium proceedings the publication of the second joint conference should prove to be an important addition to the conservators' library.

The conservation of archaeological ironwork and its storage and display is not only a pressing and complex problem for national museums, it extends to all museums and institutions involved with archaeological excavation. The symposium provided a forum where workers from many fields and disciplines, academic, museum and local authorities, could present details of their investigations for comment and discussion. This publication conveys the success of this interaction of ideas and the inclusion of the transcripts of the discussion periods indicates the lively debate that was stimulated by the papers presented.

The symposium was held in the Runciman Lecture Theatre of the National Maritime Museum, Greenwich on Friday, 4th July, 1980.

Basil Greenhill, Director
National Maritime Museum

David Wilson, Director
British Museum

EDITORIAL NOTE

The increasing amount of archaeological ironwork being excavated from both land and underwater sites necessitates a reappraisal of the conservators approach to the choice of conservation methods. This symposium was intended to provide a theoretical and practical approach to this problem rather than presenting a documentary record of the treatment of specific objects. The present volume is the result of the papers presented at this meeting.

The first paper deals with the characterisation of the corrosion products on archaeological ironwork and a description of the processes leading to their formation. The subsequent papers describe, in a logical manner, various approaches to the examination, cleaning, stabilization and storage and display of excavated ironwork. Editing of the papers has been kept to a minimum although the use of symbols and nomenclature has been standardised.

The discussions at the end of each session were recorded and have been transcribed for inclusion in this volume. Questions which were subsequently dealt with in the papers presented for publication have been omitted. There has been no attempt to rewrite the discussions although all those who contributed were given the opportunity to comment on their questions and answers.

Differing opinions were expressed on two particular points namely the form in which chlorides are present in corroded iron and the storage conditions, wet or dry, between excavation and treatment. Although these points were not fully resolved, the symposium provided a stimulus for discussion and further research.

R.W.C.
S.M.B.

CONTENTS

LIST OF FIGURES

LIST OF TABLES

THE NATURE OF SURVIVING IRON OBJECTS

S. Turgoose

Introduction

The stabilisation of excavated ironwork is a subject that has attracted considerable attention, but no entirely satisfactory treatment is presently available. The development of such a treatment requires knowledge of the processes occurring after excavation that lead to the deterioration of objects, and of the causes of these processes. The breakup of artifacts is generally attributed to the presence of chloride ions (Organ, 1977), and for this reason many treatments are carried out with the intention of removing chloride ions from the corrosion products. To develop an effective method for the removal of chloride ions from corroded objects further information is needed.

First, the form in which the chloride ions are present must be known and there is no general agreement on this matter. The traditional belief that the chlorides are present as ferric chloride still survives (Organ, 1977; Nosek, 1978), though recently it has been suggested that the predominant chloride-containing compound in marine iron is iron oxychloride, FeOCl (North and Pearson, 1975). Ferrous chloride (Nosek, 1978) has also been reported, as has β-FeOOH (akaganéite) (Zucchi, Morigi and Bertolasi, 1977), which may also contain chloride ions.

Second, the reasons why chloride ions are present in the object must be known. By removing the causes of the high chloride content the removal of chloride ions may be achieved. There is very little discussion on this matter that is consistent with the well established chemistry of the species involved.

In addition to the chloride-containing compounds above, many other compounds have been reported on archaeological iron artifacts (Table 1). The large number of reported compounds would appear to make the description of the structure of excavated objects rather complicated, but it is often not clear whether these compounds were present at the time of excavation or were formed afterwards.

It would seem valuable therefore to attempt to describe the structure of excavated artifacts in terms of a simple model based on present knowledge of the corrosion processes and of the aqueous chemistry of iron.

Compound	Mineral name (Hey, 1975)	Reference
α-FeOOH	Goethite	North and Pearson, 1975; Zucchi *et al*, 1977
β-FeOOH	Akaganéite	Zucchi *et al*, 1977; Lehmann and Nosek, 1978
γ-FeOOH	Lepidocrocite	Zucchi *et al*, 1977
δ-FeOOH	———	North and Pearson, 1975; Lehmann and Nosek, 1978
Fe_3O_4	Magnetite	Pearson, 1972; North 1976; Zucchi *et al*, 1977
$FeCl_2$	Lawrencite	Lehmann and Nosek, 1978; Nosek, 1978
$FeCl_3$	Molysite (?)	Lehmann and Nosek, 1978; Nosek, 1978
FeOCl	———	North and Pearson, 1975; North, 1976; Lehmann and Nosek, 1978; Nosek, 1978
$Fe_3(PO_4)_2.8H_2O$	Vivianite	Farrer *et al*, 1953
$FePO_4.2H_2O$	Strengite	Farrer *et al*, 1953
FeS	Pyrrhotine	North, 1976
$FeCO_3$	Chalybite	North, 1976

Table 1. Corrosion products reported on archaeological iron.

The corrosion of iron

The corrosion of iron is an electrochemical reaction, and may be described by the two half-reactions

$$Fe \rightarrow Fe^{2+} + 2e \qquad \text{anodic} \quad (1)$$

and

$$O_2 + 2H_2O + 4e \rightarrow 4OH^- \quad \text{cathodic} \quad (2)$$

The other possible cathodic reaction, the reduction of hydrogen ions, does not occur at an appreciable rate above pH 4 (Uhlig, 1963) except, perhaps, in the presence of bacteria.

The electrical circuit between anode and cathode is completed by electronic movement in the solid phase and ionic movement in the aqueous phase.

Solid corrosion products are formed by subsequent reaction of the anodically produced ferrous ions with other components of the solution.

The thermodynamics of iron-water-anion systems

Those compounds which are thermodynamically stable under the conditions existing during burial would, if they can be formed, be expected to be present at the time of excavation. The long times available also enable the transformation of other compounds, which may be the initial products, into stable species.

The most useful way of representing the conditions under which given species are stable is by potential-pH diagrams, and that for the iron-water system is shown in Fig. 1. It is calculated, as are all the other diagrams, from the free energy data of Nriagu (1972) and Robie, Hemingway and Fisher (1978). The axes represent two of the variables in

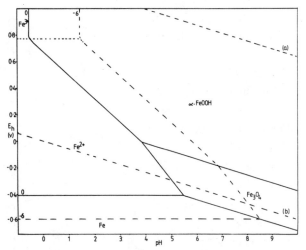

Fig. 1. Potential -pH diagram for the iron-water system.

any natural environment, redox potential (E), related to oxygen concentration, and pH. Lines (a) and (b) represent the limits of thermodynamic stability of water, given by the equations

$$E = 1.229 - 0.059pH \qquad \text{(a)}$$
$$\text{and} \quad E = 0.000 - 0.059pH \qquad \text{(b)}$$

which correspond, respectively, to the reactions

$$O_2 + 4H^+ + 4e = 2H_2O \qquad (3)$$
$$\text{and} \quad 2H^+ + 2e = H_2 \qquad (4)$$

for gas pressures of one atmosphere.

For the dissolved species contour lines may be drawn at any metal ion activity. In Fig.1 the contours are for a.Fe^{2+} = 1 and a.Fe^{2+} = 10^{-6}. The selection of a value for the activity of ferrous ions obviously has considerable effect on the diagrams and thus on the conclusions that may be drawn from them. In the study of corrosion processes it is common to find diagrams drawn for a metal ion activity of 10^{-6}, based upon the arbitrary assumption that corrosion does not occur if the equilibrium metal ion concentration in solution is less than 10^{-6}M. A corollary of this is that the metal ion activity at the surface of a corroding metal object must be greater than 10^{-6}. The value of a.Fe^{2+} = 1 is chosen as one that will not be greatly exceeded but, as will be seen later, may be achieved. The relevant redox potential and pH depend on many factors. An assessment of the conditions commonly encountered in natural waters is given by Krauskopf (1979) as being between lines (a) and (b) and between pH 4 and pH 9, although more extreme conditions do sometimes occur (Baas-Becking, Kaplan and Moore, 1960). The conditions that are relevant to a study of the formation of corrosion products are those at the points of formation of the products, and these conditions are considerably influenced by the presence of a corroding object, and will not be constant throughout the corrosion products. Since corroding iron produces ferrous ions at the metal surface the solution redox potential and the pH would both be expected to increase with distance from the metal surface. In general, slightly acidic, reducing conditions would be expected close to the metal surface.

Fig. 1 shows two stable solids, magnetite and goethite, both of which are commonly encountered on archaeological objects. Strictly, goethite is unstable with respect to $\alpha - Fe_2O_3$ (haematite), but the free energy change for reaction (5) is small

$$2\alpha - FeOOH \rightarrow \alpha - Fe_2O_3 + H_2O$$

(-2.72 kJ/mol^{-1})and goethite"can persist for geologically long times" (Krauskopf, 1979). Magnetite is stable under more reducing conditions than goethite, and so would be expected to occur between a goethite layer and the metal core, as is commonly seen.

The diagram for the iron-water system does not of course reflect the conditions occurring during burial, since all natural waters contain dissolved salts, but the presence of anions that have soluble iron salts has no effect on the diagrams. For example, the potential-pH diagram for the iron-water-chloride system, at a.Cl^- = 1, is identical to Fig. 1, and magnetite and goethite are the only solids that would be expected.

If anions which have insoluble iron salts are present other stable solids may appear. Fig.2 shows the iron-water-CO_2 diagram, for a p.CO_2 of 10^{-2} atm., a reasonable estimate of the value of groundwater. It can be seen that ferrous carbonate is the stable species under reducing conditions in neutral

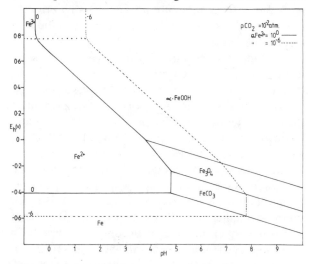

Fig. 2. Potential -pH diagram for the iron-water-CO_2 system.

and slightly acidic solutions, conditions which are possible during burial. The reported occurrence of ferrous carbonate (North, 1976), in the lower levels of a marine concretion, with magnetite and in contact with a solution of pH 4.8 can be explained by Fig.2. The potential at this point must have been about -0.25 V, i.e. the solution was slightly acidic and reducing, as would be expected.

A similar diagram may be drawn allowing for the presence of phosphate in the solution (Fig.3). Again, it can be seen that vivianite may be stable under the conditions to be expected during burial.

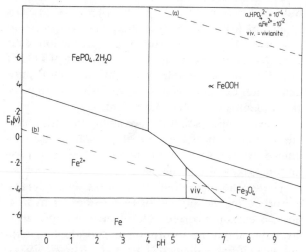

Fig. 3. Potential -pH diagram for the iron-water-phosphate system.

The object on which vivianite and strengite were found had been exposed to an anaerobic, neutral or slightly acidic solution (Farrer, Biek and Wormwell, 1953), and these conditions are perfectly compatible with the formation of vivianite. However, it does not

seem possible that strengite should form under these conditions, and it is much more likely that this compound arose from the post-excavation oxidation of vivianite.

If sulphide ions are present in the solution, various iron sulphides have regions of thermodynamic stability, and the potential-pH diagrams for this system are published elsewhere (Garrels and Christ, 1965). Thermodynamic considerations also show that reaction (6), the reduction of sulphate, should occur

$$SO_4^{2-} + 8H^+ + 8e \rightarrow S^{2-} + 4H_2O \qquad \text{(6)}$$

under reducing conditions ($E° = +0.152$ V) but, in the absence of bacteria, the reaction does not occur at a perceptible rate. If sulphate-reducing bacteria are present sulphide may be produced, and iron sulphides can result.

Not only is it the case that some compounds that are stable are not present because their formation is difficult, but there is also the possibility of the formation, as intermediates, of compounds that are not stable. The most common unstable material encountered in archaeological objects is metallic iron, but in this case there is no need to explain its formation. When considering other compounds, particularly the other forms of FeOOH, a study of the conditions under which they may be formed is instructive.

The formation of β -, γ -, and δ -FeOOH

These compounds are formed by the oxidation of anodically produced ferrous ions, and the processes occurring have been widely studied in recent years.

The oxidation of ferrous ions in chloride solution procedes, in near-neutral solutions, *via* a mixed oxidation state intermediate termed a 'green rust', and can result in Fe_3O_4, β -FeOOH or γ -FeOOH, depending on the pH and the rate of oxidation (Misawa, Kyuno, Suetaka and Shimodaira, 1971; Detournay, Derie and Ghodsi, 1976). The formation of β -FeOOH is generally associated with the rapid aerial oxidation of ferrous ions or 'green rusts', whereas slow oxidation favours the formation of magnetite.

In sulphate solutions the processes are similar, resulting in α -FeOOH, γ -FeOOH or Fe_3O_4.

Synthetic δ -FeOOH is produced by the very rapid oxidation of ferrous hydroxide in strongly alkaline solution, though recently it has been reported as a product of the atmospheric corrosion of certain steels (Misawa, Hashimoto and Shimodaira, 1974).

All of these forms of FeOOH convert in aqueous solution, over a period of a few years, to α -FeOOH, and so, even if formed on archaeological objects, would not be expected to be present in anything more than trace amounts at the time of excavation. It seems more likely that most cases of the occurrence of these compounds can be attributed to their formation after excavation, when oxidation will be more rapid. In one well established case of the occurrence of β-FeOOH this was known to be so (Zucchi et al, 1977).

The occurrence of all of the compounds listed in Table 1 has been explained except for the chlorides of iron. In view of the great importance attached to these compounds it seems worthwhile to consider them in more detail.

Chloride ions in corrosion products

The deterioration of excavated objects is often attributed to the presence of chloride, and there is no doubt that most, if not all, corrosion products on archaeological artifacts contain chloride ions. The amount can vary widely, though most reported values for marine sites are less than 2% by weight e.g. 1.6% (Pearson, 1972), 0.7-2.0% (Barkman, 1977) and 0.07-0.2% (Lehmann and Nosek, 1978). Objects from the *Batavia* show much higher chloride contents, 13-14% (North and Pearson, 1975) and 10% (North, 1976). Objects from soils might be expected to have lower chloride contents, e.g. 0.5-1.0% (Wihr, 1975).

There are three ways in which these chloride ions, or any other anions, could be present:
1. contained within a solid component of the corrosion products,
2. adsorbed on the surface of a solid component of the corrosion products, or
3. in solution in the water within the pores of the corrosion products.

Considering the first possibility, the preceding analysis does not mention any chloride-containing solids, except β-FeOOH, but other compounds have been reported, so further discussion of the chemistry of the iron-water-chloride system seems warranted.

Fig.4 shows the potential-pH diagram for the iron-water-chloride system at a chloride ion activity

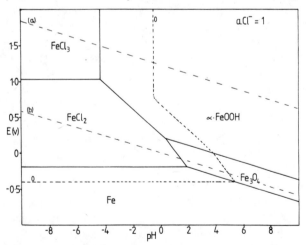

Fig. 4. Potential -pH diagram for the iron-water-chloride system.

of 1. In this diagram the solid lines represent the boundaries between the stability fields for the solids, and the contour line for a. $Fe^{2+}=1$ is shown. It can be seen that ferrous chloride is only a stable solid below pH 2, which is much more acidic than has been found or would be expected in buried objects. Also the ease of dissolution of ferrous chloride in water would preclude the existence of the solid as a metastable phase.

The conditions required for the formation of solid ferric chloride are even further removed from those that may occur during burial, and there seems to be no doubt that solid ferric chloride is not present at the time of excavation. The possibility of ferrous and ferric ions being in solution will be discussed later, as will be their formation after excavation.

The other chloride-containing solid that has been suggested as a component of the corrosion products on marine iron is iron oxychloride, FeOCl. It is not thermodynamically stable in the presence of water at ambient temperatures, and decomposes rapidly in water and even moist air (North and Pearson, 1977). The published methods of synthesising FeOCl all involve temperatures in excess of 200°C. These factors make it difficult to explain the occurrence of FeOCl, either before or after excavation, on the basis of its known chemistry. Examination of the published evidence for the presence of iron oxychloride on artifacts, an X-ray powder diffraction pattern (North and Pearson, 1975), suggests that the evidence may have been misinterpreted. The agreement between the powder picture from the corrosion products and that for FeOCl does not seem sufficient to justify the conclusion that FeOCl is present. Taking into account the origin of the sample the one compound the presence of which does seem to be indicated is cementite, Fe_3C, which will be present in all cast irons and is a major component of white cast iron. Fig.5 shows the X-ray diffraction data from North and Pearson (1975) with that of FeOCl and Fe_3C. The sample was obviously not pure cementite, but there is insufficient evidence to positively identify the other components.

Thus, it appears that the possibility that the chloride ions present at the time of excavation are contained within solid components of the corrosion products may be eliminated.

The second suggestion, that chloride ions might be adsorbed on the surface of iron oxides or hydroxides, is certainly correct. However, the information available about the adsorption of chloride, on goethite, even if finely divided (Parfitt and Russell, 1977), suggests that a chloride content greater than about 0.2% by weight cannot be explained in this way.

Having eliminated two of the three possibilities there remains the conclusion that the chloride ions must be present in solution, at the time of excavation but the concentrations required to explain the

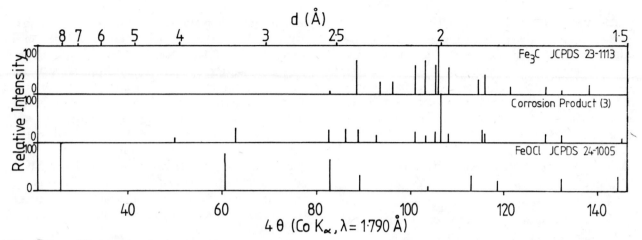

Fig. 5. X-ray diffraction data for iron corrosion products (North and Pearson, 1975), Fe_3C and FeOCl.

observed chloride contents are much higher than the concentrations that would have existed in the surrounding water during burial. In order to see if this is possible, the basic corrosion processes must be re-examined.

The corrosion of iron can be described by reactions (1) and (2). Initially these reactions will occur randomly over the metal surface, but if the oxygen supply to the surface is not uniform then the anode and cathode may become localised. The pH at the anodic areas may drop, due to ferrous ion hydrolysis, reaction (7), and that at the cathodic area may rise due to cathodically produced hydroxide ions.

$$Fe^{2+} + H_2O = FeOH^+ + H^+ \qquad (7)$$

These reactions must be accompanied by a flow of electrons in the solid phase and a flow of ions in solution; cations move from anode to cathode and anions move in the opposite direction. Since chloride is often the predominant anion in natural environments, and it possesses a high mobility in aqueous solution, much of this current will be carried by chloride ions moving towards the anodes. The extent to which this may lead to an increase in chloride concentration at the anodic area is shown by laboratory experiments.

Suzuki, Yamabe and Kitamura (1973) have studied the conditions in artificial corrosion pits on stainless steel and iron in 0.5 M sodium chloride solution (approximately the same concentration as in sea-water). On stainless steel the chloride concentration in the pits exceeded 6 M and the ferrous ion concentration was greater than 3 M. The concentrations were not measured in the case of iron but a pH of 4.8 was recorded at the anodic areas. Pourbaix (1972) has also measured the pH at an iron anode and found values between 2.7 and 4.7, although the lower figures were associated with access of oxygen to the anode compartment. These results may be compared to the pH of 4.8 found by North (1976) within the graphitised regions of a cast iron cannon-ball.

In the laboratory experiments the only reaction

that could be controlling the pH is ferrous ion hydrolysis, reaction (7). Taking the value of the equilibrium constant for reaction (7), for an ionic strength of 1.0, equation (c) (Sillen and Martell, 1964), a pH of 4.8 will be given by a ferrous ion concentration of 1.25 M and a pH of 4.7 by 2 M ferrous ion. The counter ion can only be chloride, and the corresponding concentrations are 2.5 M and 4 M, respectively, a considerable increase over the bulk chloride concentration. The lower pH in the presence of oxygen can be attributed to ferric ion hydrolysis, aqueous ferric ions being stronger acids than aqueous ferrous ions.

$$K = \frac{[FeOH^+][H^+]}{[Fe^{2+}]} = 10^{-9.7} \qquad (c)$$

If the pH of 4.8±0.1 found in the inner regions of the corrosion product is determined by ferrous ion hydrolysis, as seems likely, then this also implies that the chloride concentration of the solution at the metal surface could be 3 or 4 M, and in view of the porosity of corrosion products these concentrations seem more than adequate to explain the chloride contents of objects. Thus, there is no need to invoke the presence of chloride-containing solids, which would not be expected to be present, to explain the observed chloride content of objects at the time of excavation.

The pH measurements of North (1976) also give information as to the location of the cathode in the corrosion cell (the anode must, obviously, be at the metal surface). The pH increased steadily from 4.8 to about 6, moving out through the thick iron-stained concretion, then jumped to 8.1, the pH of the surrounding sea-water. Since the cathodic reaction produces hydroxide ions the pH at the cathodic areas cannot be less than the bulk pH, so the cathodic reaction must have been occurring at least as far from the metal surface as the outer edge of the iron-stained concretion. This, in turn, means that the corrosion products, the major components of

5

which are Fe_3O_4 and α-FeOOH, must possess electronic conductivity. Since these corrosion products are common to most excavated objects, from all environments, this conclusion should be applicable to most objects. This explains phenomena such as void formation, since the entire metal surface can act as an anode, the cathodic reaction occurring at points in the oxide layers.

The structure of excavated artifacts

It may be concluded that the structure of the corrosion products on excavated iron, from all environments, may be described in terms of a simple model. The solids present are almost entirely those that are thermodynamically stable under burial conditions; largely magnetite and goethite with perhaps some other stable ferrous compounds. Contained within the pores of this deposit is a solution that may contain high concentrations of ferrous ions, the counter ion usually being chloride. The high chloride concentration at the metal surface arises from the flow of ionic corrosion current between spatially separated anodes and cathodes. While this solution may be described as essentially a ferrous chloride solution, the widely held belief that ferric chloride is present at the time of excavation is totally erroneous. The solubility product of goethite, equation (d), is such that the maximum value that could be expected for a.Fe^{3+} is about 10^{-16} (corresponding to pH 4.8), a negligible amount.

$$(a.Fe^{3+})(a.OH^-)^3 = 10^{-43.7} \underline{\qquad}(d)$$

The processes occurring after excavation

If the above model is correct it should be possible to explain the processes that occur after excavation, and that lead to the deterioration of excavated objects.

On objects that are breaking up a reddish-brown powdery deposit may usually be seen at the place of fracture. This is usually β-FeOOH, which has been previously reported at the active areas on excavated iron (Zucchi *et al*, 1977). Sometimes this is accompanied by a very acidic yellow solution, containing ferrous, ferric and chloride ions.

There are many ways of producing β-FeOOH at ambient temperatures, but they all involve the oxidation of ferrous ions in the presence of halide ions, usually chloride. The overall reaction may be represented by the equation:–

$$4Fe^{2+} + O_2 + 6H_2O \rightarrow 4FeOOH + 8H^+ \underline{\qquad}(8)$$

If this reaction occurs near the metal surface the pH will be prevented from dropping, since the hydrogen ions produced will be consumed by reaction with the metal. However, if the oxidation occurs at points remote from the metal surface the pH will drop to a value at which the solubility of FeOOH becomes appreciable, and ferric ions will appear in solution. This explains the appearance of droplets of 'ferric chloride' solution on the surface of deteriorating objects, but it must be stressed that this 'ferric chloride' is a consequence of deterioration and not the cause. The break-up can be attributed to the precipitation of solid β-FeOOH, and the consequent introduction of stresses into the object. It is also possible that the acid produced by reaction (8) has deleterious effects on the mechanical strength of the corrosion products by causing dissolution of the oxide layers.

If the excavated object possesses a metallic core there is likely to be some ferrous ion in the object at the time of excavation, but the most important source of the ferrous ions would seem to be further corrosion after excavation. This process requires the presence of only oxygen and water, and so will not be totally prevented by the removal of chloride ions. However, the presence of chloride ions, or any other ions, will considerably increase the rate of corrosion, since dissolved salts increase the conductivity of the aqueous phase, and so removal of chloride ions will reduce the instability of artifacts.

Conclusions

The structure of excavated objects may be described in terms of a simple model. The solids present at the time of excavation are those that are thermodynamically stable under burial conditions, and contained within the pores of these solids there is what may be described as a ferrous chloride solution. This model is consistent with the present knowledge of the chemistry of the species involved and of corrosion processes. It also explains the processes occurring after excavation, and the reasons for the high chloride concentration in excavated objects.

It is hoped that this knowledge may lead to the development of more effective treatment methods, since the causes of the problems are now understood.

References

Baas-Becking, L.G.M., Kaplan, I.R. and Moore, D., Limits of the natural environment in terms of pH and oxidation-reduction potentials. *Journal of Geology. 68* 1960, pp.243-284.

Barkman, L., Conservation of rusty iron objects by hydrogen reduction. *Corrosion and Metal Artifacts*. (ed. B.F. Brown *et al*, 1977, pp.155-166. (NBS Special Publication 479, U.S. Government Printing Office, Washington D.C. 1977).

Detournay, J., Derie, R. and Ghodsi, M., Etude de l'oxydation par aeration de Fe(OH)$_2$ en milieu chlorure. *Z. anorg. allg. Chem. 427* 1976, pp.265-273.

Farrer, T.W., Biek, L. and Wormwell, F., The role of tannates and phosphates in the preservation of ancient buried iron objects. *Journal of Applied Chemistry. 3* 1953, pp.80-84.

Garrels, R.M. and Christ, C.L., *Solutions, Minerals and Equilibria*. 1965. Harper and Row, London.

Hey, M.H., *Chemical Index of Minerals*. 1975. British Museum, London.

Krauskopf, K.B., *Introduction to Geochemistry*. 1979. McGraw-Hill, London. pp.200 and 212.

Lehmann, J. and Nosek, E.M., Research and conservation of iron objects discovered in a shipwreck lifted from Gdansk gulf. *Conservation of Iron Objects Found in Salty Environments*. (ed. R.M. Organ, E.M. Nosek and J. Lehmann) 1978. pp.50-64. (Historical Monuments Documentation Centre, Warsaw).

Misawa, T., Hashimoto, K. and Shimodaira, S., The mechanism of the formation of iron oxide and oxyhydroxides in aqueous solution at room temperature. *Corrosion Science. 14* 1974, pp.131-149.

Misawa, T., Kyuno, T., Suetaka, W. and Shimodaira, S., The mechanism of atmospheric rusting and the effect of Cu and P on the rust formation of low alloy steels. *Corrosion Science. 11* 1971, pp.35-48.

North, N.A., Formation of coral concentrations on marine iron. *International Journal of Nautical Archaeology. 5* 1976, pp.253-258.

North, N.A. and Pearson, C., Alkaline sulphite reduction treatment of marine iron. *ICOM Committee for Conservation, 4th Triennial Meeting, Venice, 1975*, pp.1-13. (75/13/3).

North, N.A. and Pearson, C., Thermal decomposition of FeOCl and marine cast iron corrosion products. *Studies in Conservation. 22* 1977, pp.146-157.

Nosek, E.M., Research and conservation of the iron objects currently displayed at the salt mine museum. *Conservation of Iron Objects Found in Salty Environments*. (ed. R.M. Organ, E.M. Nosek and J. Lehmann) 1978. pp.9-20. (Historical Monuments Documentation Centre, Warsaw).

Nriagu, J.O., Stability of vivianite and ion-pair formation in the system $Fe_3(PO_4)_2$–H_3PO_4–H_2O. *Geochimica and Cosmochimica Acta. 36* 1972, pp.459-470.

Organ, R.M., The current status of the treatment of corroded metal artifacts. *Corrosion and Metal Artifacts*. (ed. B.F. Brown *et al,*) 1977, pp.107-142. (NBS Special Publication 479, U.S. Government Printing Office, Washington D.C. 1977).

Parfitt, R.L. and Russell, J.D., Adsorption on hydrous oxides IV. Mechanism of adsorption of various ions on goethite. *Journal of Soil Science, 28* 1977, pp. 297-305.

Pearson, C., The preservation of iron cannon after 200 years under the sea. *Studies in Conservation. 17* 1972, pp.91-110.

Pourbaix, M., Significance of protection potential in pitting, intergranular corrosion and stress-corrosion cracking. *J. less comm. Metals. 28* 1972, pp. 51-65.

Robie, R.A., Hemingway, B.S. and Fisher, J.R., Thermodynamic properties of minerals and related substances. *U.S. Geological Survey Bulletin 1452, 1978.*

Sillen, L.G. and Martell, A.E., Stability constants. *Chemical Society Special Publication No. 17, 1964.*

Suzuki, T., Yamabe, M. and Kitamura, Y., Composition of anolyte within pit anode of austenitic stainless steels in chloride solution. *Corrosion. 29* 1973, pp.18-22.

Uhlig, H.H., *Corrosion and Corrosion Control*. 1963. J. Wiley and Son Inc. p.85.

Wihr, R., Electrolytic desalination of archaeological iron. *Conservation in Archaelogy and the Applied Arts. IIC Congress, Stockholm, 1975*, pp.189-193.

Zucchi, F., Morigi, G. and Bertolasi, V., Beta iron oxide hydroxide formation in localised active corrosion of iron artifacts. *Corrosion and Metal Artifacts*. (ed. B.F. Brown et al) 1977, pp.103-105. (NBS Special Publication 479, U.S. Government Printing Office, Washington D.C. 1977).

RADIOGRAPHY OF ARCHAEOLOGICAL IRONWORK

M. Corfield

The application of scientific aids to the examination of archaeological material prior to conservation is a comparatively recent development. The use of radiography has only become commonplace within the last decade and in some places is still not considered routine for all but the obviously out-standing artifacts (Biek, 1969; Gilardini, Orsini and Taccani, 1977; Carter, 1978). The conjunction of the lack of understanding of the nature of the material being treated and the drastic nature of treatments employed during the 50's and 60's has left a legacy of ironwork in many museums from which all the corrosion has been removed and, of greater concern, from which decorative effects have been lost leaving the merest trace of inlay or overlay.

The information which may be gained from the radiograph is particularly dramatic, and especially so in the case of heavily mineralised ironwork (Fig.6).

Fig. 6. X-radiograph of an iron padlock. The object, as excavated, gives no clue to its identity which is clearly seen in the adjacent radiograph.

Fig. 7. X-radiograph of a Saxon buckle clearly showing inlay in the form of tangential strips on the loop and as concentric rings on the plate. The radiograph also shows the extent to which the object is corroded – indicated by the gap between the inlay and the core and the lack of any core in the lower left corner of the figure. The radiograph failed to show the presence of a plate of brass inlaid with niello on the top of the loop.

Often, when such objects are found, they appear as formless lumps of corrosion and concretion – the prime use of the radiograph has always been to determine what lies beneath the corrosion (Pearson, 1972; Ludikovsky, undated). Many ferrous objects were decorated by inlaying or overlaying with more precious metals such as copper alloys or silver for the former and silver or gold for the latter. Such decoration is readily seen on the radiograph as the inlaying metal is so much more dense than the iron (Evison, 1955a, b; Hall, Farrar, Klingelhofer and Leigh, 1978; Barton, undated; Gooriechx, undated) (Fig.7). Weapons may have been constructed using the technique of pattern welding (Fig.8) which is clearly seen in well-preserved examples (Anstie and Biek, 1961), while edged tools often have a steel cutting edge attached to a wrought iron back which

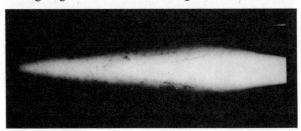

Fig. 8. X-radiograph of a pattern welded spearhead showing the three components – the core, the band of pattern welding and the blade.

may show when the two metals have different densities or if the weld between the two components can be seen (Fig.9).

Of great importance to the conservator is the revelation in the radiograph of the extent to which the object has deteriorated due to the process of corrosion. The corrosion rate may have been such that mineralisation is complete and no metal core survives. In such cases many conservation techniques are to be avoided. Equally, the object may be shown to have substantial areas of mineralisation and the conservator should again be cautious – the many examples of 'filigree' ironwork in museums

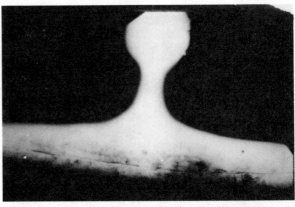

Fig. 9. X-radiograph of an axe showing the line of the weld between the cutting edge and the core.

testifies to those occasions when such objects have not been treated with caution. The corrosive effect can also penetrate deeply so that an apparently sound artifact may be deeply fissured by cracks and corrosion which, if mechanical cleaning removes the cementing material, can result in the fragmentation of the object.

In the late 60's and early 70's it became increasingly common for excavation reports to be compiled making extensive use of radiographs for drawing finds. The need for this technique to be adopted was caused by the accumulation of archaeological finds outstripping the provision of conservation facilities. As this gap between the ability of conservators to clean objects and the rate at which archaeologists excavate them widens, so the demand for a measure of selectivity to be adopted grows (Dimbleby, 1978; Keene, 1980).

The conservator cleans an artifact for a variety of reasons, and the decision to clean objects is one which he takes with the archaeologist and with the curator who will eventually be responsible for the archive. First, the excavator will want a detailed examination, including the cleaning, of those artifacts which are from particularly significant layers. Second, the curator will want those objects cleaned which will either allow the best educative display of the site to be made, or will fill a gap in the reference collections of museums.

It is important that this process of selection is carried out on a consultative basis; the archaeologist, the curator and the finds assistant should meet with the conservator, and select the objects destined for conservation making full use of the radiographs which have been taken. This small expenditure of time and thought will rescue many objects otherwise destined for oblivion.

It is because the uses of radiography are so extensive and may be senstively adapted to answer so many questions that a note of caution must be sounded. In the process of selection radiography has come to play a dominant part, and we have begun to reach a point where the radiograph has become the sole criterion for deciding the merits of the objects excavated. Notwithstanding the value of the technique important artifacts may be cast aside as not warranting treatment when, because of its limitations, radiography cannot pick out all the detail that may be encased within a corroded and concreted object.

The first, and most obvious reason why significant information is not revealed is because the quality of the radiograph is poor. Incorrect exposure is easy when vast numbers of artifacts are being screened. As the cost of X-ray plates increases the demand for economy of use grows. While it is possible to have a compromise exposure which will cope with most objects, a significant number will fall outside the range of such a screening exposure and be either under, or over-exposed (Fig.10 and 11).

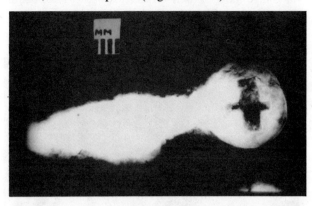

Fig. 10. X-radiograph of an Anglo-Scandinavian key showing how more than one exposure may be needed to elucidate fully the information on an object. The plating on the head and wards shows clearly. The inlay on the handle however, is entirely lost in the underexposure of this region.

Fig. 11. The cleaned key on which the inlay is seen as well as the grooves from which the inlay has been lost.

A small proportion of objects may be too bulky to be penetrated by the low energy X-rays generated by the small, self-contained units now common in many conservation laboratories. It is possible, however, to increase the potential of such equipment by recourse to exposure enhancing techniques. Lead screens above and below the film (Fig.12) will remove softer scattered radiation generated within the object and by reflection from the base of the equipment. If this scattered radiation is not removed the sharpness of the image is reduced and the detection of detail is more difficult. Scattered radiation results more from those components of the X-ray beam which are of lower energy and can be removed by inserting a copper filter between the source and the object.

The orientation of the object when it is being examined can result in loss of detail since the radiographic image is two dimensional. Although many objects are basically two-dimensional, it cannot be ignored that important detail may be on the face not examined, or that the face examined is so uniformly coated with another metal that the one masks the other.

Complex objects when laid on their natural base may have most of their surface exposed to the beam of radiation, but still have their salient points obscured. An obvious example of this is a shield boss, which when laid on its base shows most of the

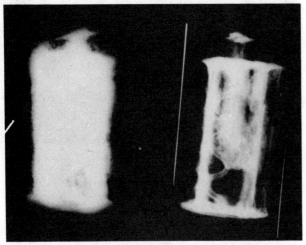

Fig. 12. These two radiographs clearly show the beneficial effects of using lead screens. The radiograph on the left is unscreened, and that on the right with screens. The detail of the padlock shows clearly; despite the great improvement seen the presence of the copper brazing materials was only revealed by cleaning.

surface of the cone but conceals important technological features, for example, the method of fabrication of the tip and the insertion of the knob into the apex, or the signs of any joint between the cap and the carination. Unfortunately, most bosses have been examined for decoration to help typological study rather than for technological reasons.

Many complex objects are brought to the conservator as concreted masses from an excavation; such objects may be resolved by stereo-radiography. In this process two separate exposures are made with a shift in the position of the object between the exposures. When viewed with a stereo-viewer such radiographs show clearly the spatial position of the components of a complex artifact (Loose, 1960). When making stereo pairs with cabinet sets it is not possible to give sufficient movements for a suitable separation of detail: this limitation can be overcome by the use of angled blocks to increase the angle of incidence of the X-ray beam. The technique also depends on the object being of sufficient thickness to benefit from stereo-radiography.

The medical technique of tomography is another possible method of separating layers within a complex artifact or group of artifacts. In this method the orientation of film and X-ray tube is so arranged that only a slice of the object being examined is in focus with the remainder reduced to an unfocused blur (Groen, 1978). The scanner X-ray systems have also been suggested as a means of examining objects and a further study of this technique for archaeological material would be of interest (Hollanders-Favart and Schoirte, 1978).

Processing can also bring a further range of faults

which may result in information not being discovered which could lift a mediocre object to a level where conservation was deemed advisable; wrong developing temperatures, exhausted solutions, incomplete washings and inefficient drying can all contribute to reduce the quality of the film. Exhausted solutions are a particular problem where the development of radiographs is sporadic, and it is to meet this problem that some industrial users are turning to the Polaroid system. Using a Polaroid type 811 film a positive image is obtained and as each film has its own developer a fresh batch is used each time. However, the final image does not give the same detail as a negative radiograph, and whilst a positive print is useful for work at the bench the negative image will remain essential for critical analysis. A negative Polaroid system is under development and this could provide the answer for those occasions when uniform results are required by the occasional user.

X-ray paper which produces a negative print and which is processed in an activator/stabiliser processor suffers from the disadvantages of both the polaroid and the negative system, that is, the inability to resolve the fine detail and the fall off of chemical activity when solutions are only used occasionally.

The conditions under which the radiograph is viewed are often unsatisfactory. It is usual for the object to be exposed in such a way that the person viewing it can do so at the laboratory bench, and usually with whatever light source is available. A correctly exposed radiograph cannot be viewed in this way, but should be examined in a darkened room on a viewer fitted with blinds to obscure all unwanted light, or occasionally by means of a high intensity viewer. Seen in this way minute detail becomes evident, and that which was previously obscure becomes clear. A further refinement is to use a microscope or a magnifying lens to examine the image even more closely. Not only will technological detail be revealed by these means but the conservation work will be aided by a better knowledge of the nature of the object. Sadly many conservators and archaeologists continue to examine radiographs by holding them to the light; to see anything in this way the X-ray must be underexposed and as the viewer's eye will be attempting to pick out detail on a dark radiograph against a bright background it will often be beyond the accommodation of the pupil.

Moving from the techniques of radiography the nature of the object being examined must also be considered. Some detail may not be revealed on the radiograph because of its nature, while conversely information may be seen on the radiograph which cannot be revealed by cleaning.

Of the former, organic materials form the largest and most obvious group which will rarely show. Such material may be preserved in its original form by the antiseptic action of the corrosion process, but will more usually be seen as a 'replacement' where the cells of the organic material have been infused with corrosion product, the material then decaying and leaving a cast of the structure. To confirm the presence of such remains, careful probing under a microscope is essential and no object should be cast aside without such examination, nor should a conservation process be initiated lest the remains be destroyed.

A safe and relatively certain means of revealing some organic remains is by neutron radiography (Fig.13) in which neutrons are used to make an image instead of X-rays. The lower atomic mass elements are more opaque to neutrons than the higher members, thus any hydrogenous material which survives with replaced organics will be revealed by this technique. The technique can also be used to detect the remnants of fluxes used in brazing or soldering. Unfortunately it is a very expensive process and can thus only be used for especial cases (Barton, 1965). A major problem is to show the presence of thin coatings of metal such as silver or copper alloy applied for decorative or functional

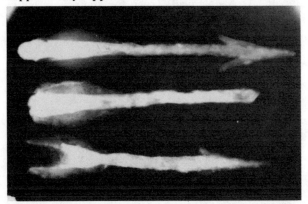

Fig. 13. Neutron radiograph of three plumbata or matriobilbi – short spearheads with lead collars. The iron shafts show with a clarity equal to that of an X-radiograph. The lead collar has been completely penetrated by the neutron beam which has been entirely absorbed by the wooden remains of the shaft.

reasons. When reasonably substantial plating survives it is usually seen as a bright white line (Fig.14) surrounding the object; sometimes the line may be within the corrosion products and will indicate the original surface. These indications of former surfaces can serve as a warning to those who would use the radiograph injudiciously as a guide to illustration. If the draughtsperson uses the outer edge of the radiographic image as the outer edge of the illustration then it can be seen that the plating line lies within this area. Alternatively, if the corrosion products are of a lower density and therefore do not show clearly on the radiograph, the well defined metal core may be mistaken for the original surface and thus will be represented as being smaller than the original.

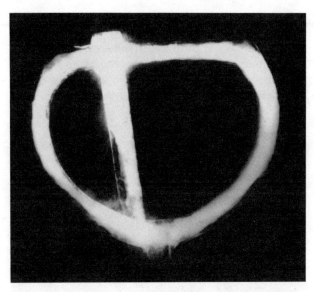

Fig. 14. X-radiograph of a medieval buckle showing the thin bright line associated with tinning or silvering. The fineness of the line at the top right of the object demonstrates the care with which radiographs should be examined.

Often, plating will not be of a sufficient thickness to show on the radiograph (Fig.15). This is the case with the thin coat of copper sometimes seen on medieval objects such as arrowheads and which can only be revealed by cleaning. Many iron objects contain minute traces of tin plate or brass within the corrosion layers; the only way of discovering this is to clean at least part of the object under the microscope. A recently noticed phenomenon is the revela-

Fig. 15. Photograph of a spearhead which clearly showed pattern welding in the radiograph, but which failed to show the silver plate on the blade.

tion of inclusions in iron corrosion products which did not show on the radiograph and which were shown on further investigation to be ferrous based (Fig.16). Clearly for a better understanding of the techniques of the metal worker in antiquity such phenomena require investigation and documentation. It also suggests that when we do get 'thin bright line' phenomena we should be very wary of designating tinning without further proof – proof which may be supplied quite simply sometimes by microscopic examination.

Occasionally detail will be revealed in the radiograph which cannot be exposed to view. For example, the corrosion products of silver are more opaque to X-rays than those of iron; therefore although

Fig. 16. Photomicrograph of the surface of an iron object showing a triangular inclusion which on subsequent analysis was identified as ferrous based. Such features cannot be revealed by radiography.

an object may be shown in the radiograph to be decorated, when the iron corrosion is removed only a layer of slightly less dense corrosion product indicates the position of the corroded overlay or inlay (Fig.17).

The most humble appearing objects may prove important to the site when subjected to radiographic examination. Few would have expected that when a

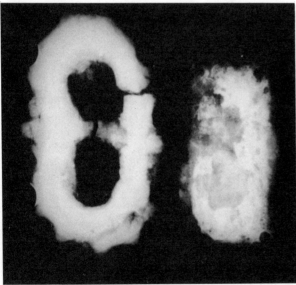

Fig. 17. Radiograph of a Saxon buckle. The scalloped edge of the loop was formerly inlaid and two semilunar pieces of inlay survive. The detached plate shows in lighter tones the remains of a silver overlay. On investigation the overlay was found to be entirely mineralised and thus could not be revealed.

group of what were thought to be nails were examined one of them would turn out to be a unique iron strap end. This does underline the point that all iron objects should be examined radiographically and the temptation to put to one side those objects from which little additional information is expected

be avoided. It is gratifying that the Department of the Environment recognise this need and that specific provision is made for examining material from rescue excavations funded by them.

It is clear that a radiographic approach must have a certain finesse, it is not enough to adopt a blanket coverage as this is to equate radiography with snapshot photography. A partial solution to the problem of the inadequacy of mass radiography would be to make the selection process much more rigorous, to insist that plates and objects are seen together in optimum viewing conditions by all of the specialists concerned with the excavation archive; to refine the processing techniques; and to take a proportion of those objects which are not to be conserved and clean selected areas. If this can be done, it may be that past technological practices are revealed as being much richer and more complex than they have previously been described. One can also feel confident that one is applying selective methods within the framework of ethics that the conservation profession demands.

Acknowledgements

I am grateful to Kate Foley and Robert White of the Lincoln Archaeological Trust for their help and advice in preparing this paper.

References

Anstie, J.W. and Biek, L., A study of pattern welding. *Medieval Archaeology. 5* 1961, pp.71-93.

Barton, J.P., Radiology using neutrons. *Studies in Conservation. 10* 1965, p.135.

Barton, K.J., Discovery and treatment of an inlaid scabbard. *Discovery. 21.*

Biek, L., Artifacts. *Science in Archaeology; A Survey of Progress and Research.* (ed. D. Brothwell and E. Higgs) 2nd Ed. 1969, Thames and Hudson, London. pp.567-570.

Carter, G.F., Archaeological Chemistry II. *American Chemical Society Advances in Chemistry Series 171,* 1978.

Dimbleby, G.W., *The Scientific Treatment of Materials from Rescue Excavations.* Directorate of Ancient Monuments and Historic Buildings, Department of the Environment, 1978.

Evison, V.I.,a, Early Anglo-Saxon inlaid metalwork. *Antiquaries Journal. 35* 1955, pp.20-45.

Evison, V.I.,b, Anglo-Saxon finds near Rainham, Essex. *Archaeologia. 96* 1955, pp.159-196.

Gilardini, A., Orsini, R.A. and Taccani, S., *X-rays in Art, Physics – Technique – Application.* Gilardoni, Mandello Lario (Como). 1977.

Goorieckx, D., Methods of examining and treating Merovinian buckles inlaid with silver. *Bulletin of the Institute of Royal du Patrimoine Artistique. 3.*

Groen, C., The use of tomography in analysis of maritime archaeological material. *First Southern Hemisphere Conference on Maritime Archaeology, Perth, Western Australia, 1977.* pp.144-145.

Hall, R.A., Farrar, R.A., Klingelhofer, A.G.S., and Leigh, D. A Viking age grave at Donnybrook, Co. Dublin. *Medieval Archaeology. 22* 1978, pp.64-83.

Hollanders-Favart, D. and van Schoitre, R., Amelioration des techniques radiographiques le scanning. *ICOM Committee for Conservation, 5th Triennial Meeting, Zagreb, 1978.* (78/1/14).

Keene, S.V., (ed), *Conservation, Archaeology and Museums. Occasional Paper No. 1.* UKIC, 1980.

Loose, L., La stereoradiograpie. *Studies in Conservation. 5* 1960, p.85.

Ludikovsky, K., X-ray photography of metals in archaeology. *Archaeologicke Rozhledy 9.*

DISCUSSION

Chairman:
M.W. Pascoe

F. Schweizer

I think it will be hard to prove that there are no oxychlorides in the corrosion products, but if you determine the chloride content in a corroded land excavated iron object it is approximately 0.2%. Are your conclusions that oxychlorides do not play an important part in the destruction of an object based on theoretial or actual determinative considerations?

S. Turgoose

It's theoretical in the sense that you can never prove experimentally that something is not there. What I'm saying is that there is no need to assume any chloride containing compounds at all at this level of 0.2%. A further point about FeOCl is that when you put it into water it has decomposed within 2-3 minutes.

F. Schweizer

We have synthesised FeOCl and you can wash it with water for at least 30 minutes and X-ray defraction presents no problems.

S. Turgoose

North and Pearson have given rate constants for the kinetics of decomposition of FeOCl and I have found that it starts to release chlorides the instant you put it into water, and releases them very rapidly. I don't think there is any evidence that there is any FeOCl in the object because at a level of 0.2% you would not detect it. Did you synthesise the FeOCl at high temperature and have you any evidence of its presence in the corrosion products?

F. Schweizer

We heated $FeOCl_3.6H_2O$ to 280°C and distilled the water off. We have evidence of insoluble chlorides, water insoluble chlorides, in the iron corrosion products; not absorbed onto the geothite.

S. Turgoose

How do you know they are not adsorbed? If you take goethite and keep washing it with water it will keep chlorides on the surface and, in fact, the degree of adsorption is sufficient to allow for the majority of chlorides in a large number of land excavated iron objects. There are some where you cannot account for all the chlorides on the basis of adsorption. You can adsorb up to about $200 \mu mol$ $Cl^- g^{-1}$ goethite, which I worked out to be about 0.5% of the goethite present and the goethite might represent 30 to 40% of the deposit. You have therefore, in the region of

0.1 to 0.3% chloride which you can account for purely on the basis of adsorption and that will not be released easily. Also β–FeOOH contains chlorides and these will not be washed out with water either.

F. Schweizer

I hope it will become clear in our paper why we still think there are insoluble chlorides in the iron compounds.

J. Price

Would you say that haematite is a possible mineral when objects have been under fire or in destruction layers and would that appear as 'tinning or silvering' in X-radiographs? That is, it may be one of the causes of the bright lines noticed when X-ray plates are examined which could be mistaken for tinning or plating. I would say that I have seen X-rays which have been under exposed where detail does disappear. In my opinion a high intensity lamp is mandatory when examining X-rays and it is best to over expose rather than under expose.

S. Turgoose

If you are talking about high temperature you would not expect to have α–FeOOH but haematite. It starts dehydrating above about 200°C and by 400°C you would just have haematite, so if it had been in a fire you would certainly get haematite.

K. Foley

On an object that one would not expect to be tinned and apparent radiological evidence is that there is tinning, when it comes to cleaning the object you cannot find any such evidence. Perhaps tinning is therefore merely represented in the plates as a difference in density.

B. Knight

Could you explain what you think the small flecks are that you had in one of your slides?

K. Foley

I don't know what they are and I would be grateful if anybody could assist me in their identification. I first looked at them because they were very discreet and obviously apart from the corrosion products. They appeared, under the microscope, as if they might be the remains of something like tinning. I had them milliprobed but no trace of any non-ferrous metal was found which leaves me wondering what they are; they could be important or quite gratuitous. I have observed these flecks in a number of objects.

B. Knight

Leo Biek has the theory that they are little flakes of hammer scale left in the corrosion products and presumably would be magnetite.

P. Slate

Would you expect the same type of corrosion products on articles removed from the sea as you would on objects excavated from land sites?

S. Turgoose

Yes, but the corrosion rate is probably higher. You tend to get a lot of cast iron objects so the actual physical structure may be different but I think the chemistry would still be the same. You would perhaps expect a higher percentage of chlorides because of the higher concentration in the environment.

Anon

You referred to the coatings as tinning. Several of the coatings I have looked at often turn out to be solders.

J. Cronyn

If, as it has been suggested, drying out iron is destructive what would you suggest was done instead?

S. Turgoose

If you keep the object perfectly dry it ought to be stable chemically, whether there will be physical effects I don't know. That means effectively zero relative humidity. At relative humidities of 5 to 10% there could be sufficient moisture to provide a film of water within the object and plenty of opportunity for the access of air and therefore oxidation. My impression would be, of the methods available at present, alkaline sulphite is probably the one that solves most of the chemical deterioration problems if it could be used straight after excavation. It may not reduce the ferric corrosion products but you are certainly not getting any oxidation of the ferrous ions in an alkaline sulphite solution.

J. Cronyn

Do yo think the drying out procedure, even if you are going to take it down ultimately to zero relative humidity, is going to be disastrous?

S. Turgoose

It depends on how quickly you can do it. If it took several months it could be dangerous but it could probably be done quicker than that depending on the object and how it is dried.

B. Knight

When it comes to drawing objects from X-rays the illustrator must have the object as well as the X-ray; there is a tendency to just take the X-ray because this is simpler. The illustrator must have the three dimensional object as well as the two dimensional representation otherwise the parallax effects could result in quite large errors. Also, if you have a very corroded mass there is the problem of deciding what the orientation of the object is.

M. Corfield

The problem is of deciding where abouts in the mass of corrosion does the original surface of the object lie. Stereoradiography may help, but a disadvantage of using the small X-ray cabinet machine is that you are restricted in where you can move the plate because the tube is fixed.

J. Price

I would suggest that the positioning of the object in the X-ray beam is very important. This can be shown by X-raying a clock 2 to 3 inches either side of the main beam and then comparing the position of the cogs. You must therefore get the plates in the centre of the beam and not do too many plates at one time.

CHOOSING A CONSERVATION METHOD FOR IRON OBJECTS

J.W.B. Black

THE MACHINE AGE PLAQUE

We must accelerate the rusting process

'. . . The menace of mechanical litter in the countryside is growing almost everywhere. There is only one word for it, and that is vile.

. . . I am referring to non-disintegrating rubbish of larger proportions, most of it metal . . .

. . . Perhaps as well as trying to perfect bio-degradeable plastic, scientists ought to be seeking ways of accelerating rust, and of speedily decomposing unwanted wood and glass.'

David Gunston
(Sunday Times, 13.4.1980)

Future conservators will no doubt be endeavouring to preserve the very material that Mr. Gunston is suggesting should be destroyed – just as present day conservators struggle to avert the ravages of rusting on iron objects, large or small, fragile or sturdy, pitted or flaky, encrusted or pristine, from land or sea, hot or cold climates, wet or dry, in the company of other artifacts or alone.

One of the major problems may be in recognising a lump of red-brown agglomerate as an object and in identifying the type of object. Careful visual examination and the use of X-radiography are essential.

Once recognised, three questions need to be asked:

How can we prevent further rusting?

How can the object be cleaned? and

How should we select particular objects for conservation?

While these three areas are covered by other papers at this meeting, I feel that this may be the time to ask ourselves if we are following the right patterns. For instance, any housewife knows that steel wool scourers may be prevented from rusting by keeping them in soapy water. But we still find ourselves leaving iron objects to soak for long periods of time in water without adjusting the pH or applying the principles of corrosion inhibition. Some of us may spend precious hours at the bench working on an object which, on completion, may be left to rust away in a damp basement.

There have been many suggestions for cleaning and stabilizing iron and I feel that the conservator, in the absence of any proven method, finds himself the prisoner of choice – unable to decide which road to follow (Fig.18):

Fig. 18. 'The Prisoner of Choice'.

Obviously, the aim is to find a method where no further deterioration, physical or chemical, is allowed to occur. The object, after cleaning and stabilization, should be aesthetically pleasing and the integrity of the object preserved.

To prevent further deterioration we should therefore avoid corrosive cleaning media and high relative humidity storage and display conditions. Protective coatings may have to be applied, for instance if the objects are in high humidity surroundings or if they are likely to be subjected to frequent handling. In order to preserve the integrity of an object and make it good to look at we need to choose a method which can be controlled, is safe to both operator and object and can be carried out in the time available. The particular method chosen will depend on the size and quantity of the objects, their condition, and the reason for cleaning. The following questions may aid that decision:

–Would an X-ray suffice?

–Will the storage/display conditions be correct?

–Will the technological evidence be retained in the surface markings or crystal structure?

–Is it sensible to spend a lot of time applying controlled mechanical cleaning?

–Is there a more appropriate method?

–How will a particular treatment affect inlay, overlay, organic materials etc.?

Perhaps only by asking ourselves these questions can we honestly hope to conserve iron objects.

AN APPRAISAL OF CLEANING METHODS FOR USE ON CORRODED IRON ANTIQUITIES

S.M. Blackshaw

Introduction

Many iron artifacts which have been buried or under the sea have an incrustation overlying the iron corrosion. This incrustation has to be removed either by dry (mechanical) or wet (chemical) means before removal of the iron corrosion can proceed. Since these incrustations can be very hard and difficult to remove, wet treatments are generally favoured, especially if the artifact involved has been excavated from a wet site and stored under water prior to treatment. If a fragile object consisting only of rust has been allowed to dry out then a mechanical treatment must be used since rehydration may cause the object to split apart. Once the incrustation has been removed the cleaning of the iron artifact can proceed.

A considerable number of methods for the cleaning and stabilisation of iron have been published in the conservation literature. The cleaning methods tend to be based on four classes of treatment, these are: electrolytic reduction, electrochemical stripping, chemical stripping and mechanical stripping. Some of the stripping methods also double as stabilisation treatments since they are said to aid the removal of soluble chlorides from rusted iron. As early as 1881 the importance of chlorides in the mechanism of the rusting of iron had been recognised, although these were only thought of as being undesirable in the form of sodium chloride from sea water. The importance of iron chloride was not recognised until much more recently.

Dr. Fredrich Rathgen (1905) writing on the preservation of antiquities describes several treatments for iron being used throughout Europe. Electrolytic reduction techniques and simple chemical stripping were not reported and mechanical stripping was only recorded in conjunction with other techniques. Electrochemical stripping was carried out using 5% sodium hydroxide and zinc foil or a mixture of acetic acid, ammonium chloride, distilled water and aluminium powder. Heat treatments were also popular. Jacobi's method recommended heating the object in a forge fire which caused most of the rust to flake off, further rust removal was achieved using water or brushing. The treatment was finished by reheating the object and coating 3-4 times with linseed oil. The description continues "only in rare cases has rusting repeated itself". Perhaps the iron was frightened into submission. In Steffennen's method the object was heated over a flame before being immersed in dilute sulphuric acid. A strong chemical action was reported at the areas of rust. The iron was then neutralised in dilute sodium carbonate, washed with water and dried in an oven.

Even hydrogen reduction, attributed to Hartwich, was described in the Rathgen publication. It was said to be for small objects with a strong metal core and was presented as a cleaning rather than a stabilising technique. It was not popular since it was said to be explosive!

In all these accounts the need for iron to have a good metallic core to withstand such treatments was recognised. Steffennen also recognised that sword blades and other tools should be heated only since sudden cooling in water could cause cracks in the cutting edge.

Before cleaning an iron object the condition of the iron must be established. Although radiography is a most useful technique, it is not always available and the running cost may prevent its use as a primary screening process. The presence of an iron core can be established using a magnet or by probing the rust layer with metal probes. This may, however, be damaging. Determination of the thickness of the rust layer is important since the original surface of an object may not be at the existing iron core but within a massive rust layer.

The choice of treatments available can be viewed simply as dry or wet. If an iron core is absent and the object is composed entirely of rust, or if a small amount of core is surrounded by a massive rust layer then a dry technique for cleaning must be used. If a sound metal core is overlaid with rust, then even if the rust layer is several millimetres thick as long as the original surface is considered to be at the surface of the core a wet cleaning technique can be used. Such techniques have the advantage of being less labour intensive than the dry techniques, although careful attention has to be paid to prevent over stripping.

The type of iron, wrought or cast (North and Pearson, 1975), has also to be taken into account. Wrought iron contains a small amount of slag which appears as fibrous inclusions in the iron structure. Preferential corrosion generally occurs along these inclusions leaving the object with a ridged appearance. Grey cast iron contains flakes of graphite which are distributed throughout the structure. These are protected cathodically by the iron which corrodes preferentially leaving a relatively soft graphitized structure. Because the corrosion on wrought iron flakes off a thin corrosion layer normally remains. In the case of iron a thick graphitized layer tends to build up. This layer could be softened by wet treatments, and damaged by hydrogen evolution at the cathode during electrolysis, thus particular care should be taken that a cast iron object is not in a fragile condition before subjecting it to a wet treatment. Wrought and cast iron can be distinguished by a metallographic examination of the microstructure but the difference may be obvious from an examination of the corrosion layer.

Another factor to be considered is the stability of the iron. If the iron is stable, i.e. there is no further occurrence of rusting, there will be no need to apply a stabilisation treatment and a wet cleaning treatment should be avoided since it would be possible for chloride contamination to occur during such a treatment if pure chemicals and deionised water are not used.

Having decided whether the iron can withstand a wet or a dry treatment the next decision is what treatment to use. This decision should be based on the thickness of the rust layer to be removed and the necessity for stabilisation. It is obviously a saving in time to combine the two, which can be done using electrolytic or electrochemical reduction. The choice of other stripping techniques will be dependent on the thickness of rust layer to be removed. The type of iron, archaeological or ethnographical also has to be considered. Ethnographic iron will normally have a light covering of rust which can be more readily removed, often by softening and abrading, than the much thicker layers on archaeological iron.

Removal of calcareous surface deposits
(Kalish, 1965; Plenderleith and Werner, 1971)

The difficulty encountered in removing surface deposits from iron objects will be dependent on whether the deposit is powdery or compact and the amount of the surface covered. A powdery, or loosely adhering deposit can be removed by light brushing possibly with the aid of running water. A compact deposit or incrustation which covers only a small area of the surface should be removed either mechanically with or without the help of softening in water, or chemically using a solution which will not attack the iron extensively, such as aqueous solutions of 10% sodium hexametaphosphate, 5% oxalic acid or 5% ammonium acetate. Objects with a fairly

continuous surface incrustation can be treated with solutions which will react more rapidly with the deposit such as EDTA disodium salt at pH 7.5, this being the optimum pH for complexing calcium (West, 1974), sulphuric, acetic and formic acid. The acids however can also attack the underlying rust and iron. As the iron cannot be examined properly until the deposit has been removed care should be taken that these solutions are not in contact with areas of exposed iron for too long.

The effectiveness of these treatments, in terms of weight loss, has been assessed on nails (from a burial site) covered with a calcareous deposit (Table 2). The samples were immersed in the solutions for 24h, then removed, brushed with a soft tooth brush, washed in distilled water, soaked in acetone and dried in an oven at 100°C. After weighing the treatments were continued for a further 48h.

A visual examination revealed that the solutions which removed the deposit most satisfactorily and caused least damage to the exposed iron corrosion were sodium hexametaphosphate, oxalic and ammonium acetate. Removing the deposit by soaking in water combined with mechanical cleaning took more time but had little effect on the iron surface. However if the iron was active rusting would take place in the water. Dilute sulphuric acid and formic acid had a very detrimental effect on the exposed iron surface, both stripping a considerable amount of rust. Since the nails were not covered uniformly with incrustation the measurements are not directly comparable with the visual observations. It is particularly interesting to note that the nail immersed in sulphuric acid dissolved during the 72h treatment.

Mechanical removal of rust from artifacts

Mechanical removal of rust can be carried out using a range of techniques and tools chosen according to the thickness of the layer to be removed and the size and strength of the artifact. Whereas a hammer and chisel can be taken to a massive corrosion layer in a cannon it would be inappropriate to apply the same technique to a rust layer covering a thin brooch.

Aqueous Solution	%Wt change after treatment	
	24h	72h
10% sodium hexameta-phosphate	−7.4%	−11.2%
Soaking in water deposit removed mechanically	−21.1%	−56.8%
5% ammonium acetate	−9.9%	−50.2%
5% acetic acid	−13.0%	−38.9%
5% oxalic acid	−3.5%	−5.4%
5% formic acid	−15.3%	−34.1%
5% EDTA disodium salt at pH 7.5	−8.5%	−16.5%
5% sulphuric acid	−69.9%	sample dissolved during treatment

Table 2. Removal of calcareous surface deposits from corroded iron objects by treatment with various aqueous solutions.

However, with the careful use of electric vibrotools, dental drills with interchangeable burrs and brushes, and compressed air drills, metal probes and pin vices a layer of rust can be worked back to the surface of the iron core or the original surface of the artifact. Rust layers can also be removed by sand blasting. This is not a method suitable for removing thick layers of rust, but can be used to advantage on thin layers as long as the rust is softer than the underlying metal and the operator is careful not to blast exposed areas of iron since this could cause pitting and surface loss.

Mechanical removal of rust (and of incrustations) has one big advantage over any other method; that is the operator has total control over the areas of rust removed and the extent to which they are removed and there need be no cleaning of exposed iron surfaces. Etching of such surfaces can be a problem if an uneven rust layer is removed chemically especially if the underlying surface was polished and the conservator hopes to repolish it. Very thin layers or patches of rust can be removed with the aid of a rust softener such as a paraffin oil or Plusgas A (Plenderleith and Werner, 1977). The oil is painted over the area of rust and left for a few hours; the rust is then removed by rubbing with emery paper. This technique is normally used on lightly rusted polished objects. As well as being time consuming, mechanical cleaning has two other disadvantages both arising from operator inexperience. One is that the surface from which the rust is being removed can be gouged or scratched. The other is that an original surface can be 'mistaken', resulting in the object being re-shaped.

Chemical removal of rust from artifacts

Chemical stripping techniques can be divided into three sub sections, electrolytic, electrochemical and chemical. Electrolytic and electrochemical methods are also used for the stablisation of iron i.e. removal of chloride ions. When removing a thick layer of rust from an artifact it is beneficial to remove some of the corrosion mechanically before undertaking chemical stripping.

a. Electrolytic cleaning (Kalish, 1965; Plenderleith and Werner, 1971; Hamilton, 1976).
Rust removal during electrolytic cleaning is achieved by the action of hydrogen evolved at the surface of the iron object. The electrolyte used is either sodium hydroxide or sodium carbonate although the use of potassium hydroxide and sulphuric acid have also been cited. If large quantities of electrolyte are to be handled sodium carbonate is the most sensible choice since it is not harmful to the operator but the treatment with sodium carbonate does take longer than that with sodium hydroxide.

The iron object is made the cathode and is suspended between two anodes made of either stainless or mild steel. Molybdenum stabilised stainless steel anodes have been used successfuly at the British Museum. Two disadvantages of stainless steel have been identified by Organ (1973). At low current density not enough oxygen is produced at the anode to prevent stainless steel being corroded and chloride ions which are extracted from the object during the treatment do not react with stainless steel causing a build up of chloride ions in the electrolyte. Implicit in this statement is the assumption that mild steel does react with chloride ions which it has not been possible to prove or disprove. If this did happen its importance lies in the number of times it is necessary to change the electrolyte during a stablisation treatment.

Electrolysis is carried out using direct current at 3-12v. Variable current densities are specified in the literature. Kalish (1965) specifies. $0.2-10A$ dm^{-2} $(2-100mA$ $cm^{-2})$. Hamilton (1976) suggests $0.1A$ cm^{-2} $(100mA$ $cm^{-2})$. North and Pearson (1978) used $10A$ m^{-2} $(1mA$ $cm^{-2})$ on the Cook cannon. The most useful criteria is the higher the current, the greater the evolution of hydrogen and the greater the mechanical action at the surface of the iron object. The reactions at the anode and the cathode produce oxygen and hydrogen.

Anode reaction:- $2H_2O - 4e \rightarrow O_2 + 4H^+$ _____(9)
Cathode reaction:- $2H_2O + 2e \rightarrow H_2 + 2OH^-$ _____(10)

The positive ions of the electrolyte migrate to the cathode and the negative ions migrate to the anode making the technique suitable for the stabilisation of iron since chloride ions from the object should be drawn towards the anode. If stripping is not required stabilisation should be carried out at low current densities so that the evolution of hydrogen is small.

During the electrolysis corrosion products on the iron are reduced. It has often been suggested that the reduction is to metallic iron but North and Pearson (1978) suggest that the reduction is to black magnetite (Fe_3O_4). During electrolysis iron objects often assume a black colouration.

This is a very useful technique if a suitable container, electrodes and power supply are available. It is readily controlled by altering the current applied, but patches of metal surface can be etched as the treatment to remove other areas of rust continues.

b. Electrochemical cleaning (Kalish, 1965; Plenderleith and Werner, 1971; Hamilton, 1976)
This is another technique which relies on the mechanical effect of hydrogen evolved in situ to remove rust. Usually zinc and sodium hydroxide or aluminium and sodium hydroxide are used. Other electrolytes such as sodium carbonate and sodium bicarbonate have been recommended in the literature, but with these the reaction progresses very slowly.

The metals can be used either as thin foils wound around the iron object or in a granulated form. In the latter case the object is simply immersed in the sodium hydroxide solution and the granules of metal added. This method has also been recommended for the stablization of iron. In this technique a galvanic cell is set up in which the iron object becomes cathodic and the zinc or aluminium become anodic. Hydrogen is evolved at the surface of the iron and chloride ions migrate from the iron object towards the anodic metal. These reactions are similar to those occurring during electrolytic reduction. During the process the anodic metals become 'passivated' by the formation of a surface layer of oxide. The main disadvantage of the technique is that it is difficult to control the evolution of hydrogen and therefore the cleaning effect. The other disadvantage arises from the passivation of the zinc or aluminium which disrupts the process.

This technique appears to be only effective with light rust layers. Compact thick rust layers require a prolonged treatment which often includes replacing the zinc or aluminium making the method expensive if a large object is to be treated, although the zinc can be reactivated by stripping with hydrochloric acid.

c. Chemical cleaning of iron

There are many rust stripping solutions sold commercially for industrial and domestic use. Most of the solutions used in conservation derive from these sources. The materials brought to the attention of the British Museum Conservation Department can be divided into three chemical types. Sequestering agents, organic acids and phosphoric acid.

i. Sequestering agents

The most common sequestering agent used for stripping iron is ethylenediaminetetra-acetic acid (EDTA). Since EDTA is only slightly soluble in water it is modified with sodium hydroxide for use as a stripping agent. The EDTA disodium salt which has a pH of 4.5 in a 5% aqueous solution is often used in conservation even though the optimum pH for EDTA to complex FeII and FeIII are 5 and 1 respectively.

Modified solutions of EDTA produced for industrial use are also used in conservation. At the British Museum Detarex C, a solution of EDTA modified with sodium hydroxide to the tetra-sodium salt at pH 13, has been used for stripping iron for many years. The sodium hydroxide dissolves some of rust which is then complexed by the EDTA. Another of the Detarex range, Detarex HM, has recently been tested. This is a solution of the sodium salt of NN-di(2hydroxy ethyl) glycine at pH 12. Other ranges of sequestering agents are available in the UK under the brand name Nervanaid, Metaquex and Dequest. Although these materials are very effective complexing agents for iron they react slowly as stripping agents. Their main use is in stripping thin layers of rust or removing rust when the extent of removal needs to be carefully controlled.

ii. Organic acids

Oxalic, thioglycollic and citric acid have been reported as stripping solutions for iron. In practice although solutions of oxalic acid are useful for removing iron stains it removes rust layers very slowly and is therefore not recommened. Thioglycollic acid used as directed by Stambolov at 28.4g per 100ml water altered to pH 7 with ammonia removes rust rapidly. It will readily attack exposed iron surfaces causing considerable damage but it can be used to remove uniform layers of rust as long as the progress of the treatment is monitored. The method is not widely used.

The use of citric acid for removing corrosion from both iron and copper based antiquities has more recently passed into disuse amongst conservators. Two commercial stripping agents, Modalene and Biox which are apparently based on citric acid have recently been brought to the attention of the Conservation Department at the B.M. The infrared spectra of both materials are similar to that of citric acid but other components have been identified in Biox. Both materials were supplied as a solution and as a paint on gel. Modalene was supplied in two strengths identified as single and double strength. Using freshly supplied solutions rust layers can be removed within 24h; this being more rapid than with a 5% citric acid solution. After 1 year the activity of the solutions decreased and a longer treatment period was required. Both Modalene and Biox etched exposed metal surfaces and Biox also caused staining not attributable to re-rusting on a polished mild steel surface. The solutions were more effective rust removers than the paint on gels, although these have an obvious application on objects too large to soak. Several applications of the gels are required to remove thin rust layers and they seem mostly suited to the removal of rust from industrial archaeology artifacts.

iii Phosphoric acid

Orthophosphoric acid is used as the basis of many of the rust remover solutions sold in retail outlets. Names such as Jenolite, Naval jelly and Trustan will be familiar to those who have fought to maintain their cars against encroaching rust. In these products rust removal and prevention are combined (Trotman-Dickenson, 1973).

The mechanical removal of all loose and thick rust layers is advocated before the solutions, which contain phosphoric acid and either zinc or manganese ions, are applied. The formation of a soluble iron phosphate results in the removal of some of the rust from the metal surface. A zinc or manganese phosphatized protective coating is then formed on the iron surface. This consists of a tertiary zinc or manganese phosphate and secondary ferrous phosphate giving a smooth pale grey or coarse black surface finish. These materials have been used to treat cannon balls after stabilisation. Although the protective layers do not last forever, in a reasonably dry environment they do give some protection. These cleaning agents have a greater application in the conservation of industrial iron artifacts than in that of archaeological iron. Ferroclean, a rust remover sold for conservation purposes reacts very similarly to a 50% solution of Orthophosphoric acid. The acid can be used as a rust remover with varying efficiency depending on the strength used. A 50% solution removes rust very quickly, but also attacks the underlying iron causing considerable etching. Used at low concentrations (5-10%) it removes rust slowly leaving the iron surface a blue/grey colour.

mechanical methods they all etch exposed iron surfaces. The importance of this is debatable. It is obviously important to maintain a polished surface, but heavy rusting will often have caused bad pitting on the suface of an archaeological object and some etching during stripping could probably be tolerated. The problems of etching can be avoided with mechanical cleaning but this has its own problems if the operator is inexperienced, or if the volume of material to be worked on is large. The arguments of aesthetic versus time considerations can only be dealt with by the working conservator and the archaeologist since each situation will undoubtedly be unique.

Acknowledgements

I would like to thank Miss S.E. Ward for her assistance with the experimental work and Dr. V.D. Daniels for his useful advice and encouragement.

Aqueous Solution	%Wt change after treatment	
	24h	72h
Electrolysis in 5% sodium hydroxide at 6v,500mA	− 3.2%	− 4.3%
Electrolysis in 5% sodium carbonate at 6v, 500mA	− 0.52%	− 3.8%
Electrochemical reduction 5% sodium hydroxide/aluminium	+ 1.3%	+ 5.2%
5% EDTA disodium salt pH 4.5	− 3.8%	− 5.9%
Ferroclean	− 7.9%	− 9.6%
Modalene	− 7.0%	− 9.2%
5% citric acid	− 6.7%	− 10.6%
5% phosphoric acid	− 6.8%	− 7.4%
28.4% thioglycollic acid at pH7	− 11.07%	− 22.5%
Detarex HM	− 0.76%	− 1.5%

Table 3. Removal of iron corrosion by treatment with various aqueous solutions.

Comparative tests on chemical cleaning methods

A comparative test was made of twelve stripping methods. Corroded iron plates were weighed, treated for 24h, washed, soaked in acetone and dried at 100°C to constant weight. The treatments were then continued for a further 48h and the plates reweighed. The treatments and results are set out in Table 3. In most cases at 24h a light layer of rust formed over the surface of the plates during drying. The surface finishes after 72h varied from black to rust brown. A black finish was produced by electrolysis with sodium hydroxide and sodium carbonate. A grey finish was produced by Ferroclean, Modalene, Biox, citric acid and thioglycollic acid and a blue grey finish was the result of treatment with phosphoric acid. After treatment with EDTA and Detarex the surface of the plates were covered with a layer of rust.

Conclusions

The methods for cleaning iron described in this paper all have one thing in common, they are not ideal. There is no one method which is suitable for use on all types of rusted iron. Although the wet methods are much less labour intensive than the dry

References

Hamilton, D.L., *Conservation of Metal Objects from Underwater Sites: A Study in Methods.* 1976. Texas Memorial Museum Miscellaneous Papers No.4.

Kalish, M., The use of electrochemical and electrolytic treatment of mineralised metal as practiced by soviet restoreers. *ICOM Committee for Conservation,* 1965.

North, N.A. and Pearson, C., Investigations into methods for conserving iron relics recovered from the sea. *Conservation in Archaeology and the Applied Arts. Stockholm Conference,* 1975, pp.173-182.

North, N.A. and Pearson, C., Methods for treating marine iron. *ICOM Committee for Conservation, 5th Triennial Meeting, Zagreb,* 1978, pp.1-10. (78/23/3).

Organ, R., Book Review: Conservation of Antiquities and Works of Art, H.J. Plenderleith and A.E.A. Werner. *Studies in Conservation. 18* 1973, pp. 189-194.

Plenderleith, H. J. and Werner, A.E.A., *The Conservation of Antiquities and Works of Art.* 2nd Ed. 1971. Oxford University Press, London

Rathgen, F., *The Preservation of Antiquities.* 1905. Cambridge University Press.

Trotman-Dickenson, A.F., *Comprehensive Inorganic Chemistry.* 1973. Pergamon Press, Oxford.

West, T.S., *Complexometry with EDTA and Related Agents.* 1974. BDH Chemicals Ltd., Poole.

Appendix

Biox: Unibond Ltd., Tuscam Way Industrial Estate, Camberley, Surrey GU15 3DD.

Detarex C and Detarex HM: W.R. Grace Ltd., Detarex Division, Northdale House, North Circular Road, London NW10 7UH.

Modalene: Modastic Ltd., 88-96 Bridge Road East, Welling Garden City, Herts AL7 1JW.

DISCUSSION

Chairman:

J.M. Black

J. Black

The last set of tests Mrs. Blackshaw showed were on pieces of mild steel. Does anybody want to take up the discussion on where do tests on new materials depart from our work on conservation methods with actual objects?

K. Foley

If you are dealing with archaeological material which may have a lot of information buried in the encrustations and this may not have been recovered radiologically, I'm not sure whether this might not be the most ethical way of handling that material. Also, neither of you that showed slides of the air-abrasive machine showed it in conjunction with a set of eye glasses or a microscope. I think it crucial that one should be pursuaded to use a microscope.

S. Blackshaw

I agree, and we are becoming increasingly aware of the material that can be lost by not using such equipment. The sloping top of the cabinets provided does make it difficult for microscope work however.

D. Watkinson

In the next issue of UKIC Conservation News (No 12 July 1980) there will be a note on how to convert, inexpensively, an ordinary stereo-miscroscope into one with a large depth of field.

M. Corfield

We have made our own cabinet with a small window in the top and a much lower top surface. We find this much more suitable.

B. Knight

I would also add that when using the air-abrasive, one should wipe the inside of the glass regularly and change the glass at intervals as this improves the vision.

M. Parrott

When cleaning iron with chemicals you have to wash them out afterwards and that usually means water and so you are back to where you started. The same is true of the Biox and Modalenes.

S. Blackshaw

They are all aqueous solutions and really you have got to make the decision as to whether or not you can put the object into water in the first place. If you decide you can, then washing with water is not going to be any more disastrous. You should perhaps put the object into an alkaline solution to minimise rusting. Hot washing always seems to cause tremendous rusting.

R. Janaway

Maddin, Muhly and Wheeler (Scientific American, 1978) have detected structures such as pearlite as an 'oxidised relic' in the outer layers of the corrosion products. What, from the archaeo-metallurgy point of view, is the importance of the outer corrosion products which puts into question the problem of how much do we clean?

J. Black

The outer corrosion products obviously are going to be what's left of what was the surface of the object. If the object underwent a surface treatment during manufacture and you then remove the corroded outer layer you may be removing evidence of this manufacture because of a relic structure left behind.

R. Lewendon

How do you determine the position of the original surface especially where you have a considerable depth of corrosion products present?

J. Cronyn

The inclusion of sand grains within the corrosion products is one marker that you are still in the corrosion in the surrounding soil rather than at the position of the original surface. If you are working down with an air abrasive machine using a magnifying system, as soon as you stop getting the inclusion of sand grains, quartz particles or whatever you know you are close to the original surface, but you must use magnification.

B. Knight

With experience you can see a difference between the layers. It might be said that the original surface is the boundary between the goethite layer, which appears reddish-brown, and the magnetite layer, which appears greyish-black. You can see this boundary quite clearly under the miscroscope as you clean down with the air-abrasive. That rather begs the question of whether it is the original surface, but you can distinguish the layers.

F. Schweizer

Do you have any indication with your stripping agents how much the loss in weight is due to actual rust removed and how much is due to the removal of iron? Many of the agents you mentioned are certainly going to dissolve some iron.

S. Blackshaw

If I had continued the experiments until all the rust was removed I could then have made some evaluation as to the attack on the iron, but I did not do this. They will all certainly attack iron but the EDTA based treatments less so than say the phosphoric or thioglycollic acid derivatives.

21

D. Barker

BISRA have carried out a lot of work on the pickling of steel and you can use up to 50% acid to which corrosion inhibitors such as hexamine has been added. The weight loss in 30% acid after about 4 to 5 hours is virtually zero. You could put inhibitors into all those systems Mrs. Blackshaw described, the rust will be dissolved but once you come to the bare metal surface any further corrosion will be prevented. In the steel industry you can remove quite thick rust layers in 2 to 3 hours. Electrolytically, you can speed up the process by using an acid electrolyte and making the object the cathode, where thick rust layers can be removed within 2 minutes but I would not like to hazard a guess as to what damage it wold do to archaeological material.

THE HYDROGEN REDUCTION PROCESS FOR THE CONSERVATION OF FERROUS OBJECTS

B.D. Barker, K. Kendell and C.O'Shea

Introduction

The use of hydrogen reduction for the treatment of archaeological iron artifacts was first employed in Sweden in 1964 to conserve the large quantities of material associated with the Swedish warship, *Wasa*. The process consisted of passing pure hydrogen over the objects which were contained within a cylindrical furnace, at a temperature between 600-700°C for 76 hours followed by cooling to ambient temperatures over a 48 hour period. Furnace conditions as low as 300°C and as high as 1000°C, have been utilised however, depending upon the nature of the artifacts being treated. The results obtained from this technique proved to be satisfactory although several problems were highlighted, in particular, the decarburization of the metal surface (Arrhenius, Barkman and Sjostrand, 1973; Barkman, 1977).

The excavation of Henry VIII's flagship, *Mary Rose*, which sank off Portsmouth in 1545 produced an analogous situation to that found in Sweden where a large number of artifacts have to be treated in a fairly short period of time. Of notable archaeological interest, were the wrought iron cannons which dictated the final size of the operational unit which was installed in the Conservation Department of Portsmouth City Museum in January 1975.

Operating procedures of Portsmouth City Museum's hydrogen furnace

A schematic diagram of the furnace and ancillary equipment is shown in Fig.19. The overall dimensions of the furnace is 4m high by 2.2m diameter and is heated by means of a 3 phase supply powering three separate banks of electric heaters which are arranged vertically. Each bank has individual controls to ensure even temperature distribution over the total height of the furnace. The retort is made of a nimonic alloy and has an effective working area of 2.5m by 0.7m diameter.

Anhydrous liquid ammonia is heated to 850°C and the resultant gas is passed over a porous nickel catalyst which is held at this temperature. The ammonia is completely dissociated into hydrogen and nitrogen and fed directly into the retort. This mixture will subsequently be referred to as 'cracker gas'.

The stages in the conservation of iron work recovered from archaeological sites may be summarised as follows:–

i. Initial pretreatment of the artifacts consists of removing any loosely adhering soils and, in the case of cannons, to clear the bore. The aim of this preliminary process is to improve the free circulation of cracker gas over the metal surface.

ii. the artifact is secured to the base and the retort clamped down over it so as to ensure an air tight seal.

iii. The ammonia cracker is allowed to come to the operating temperature of 850°C.

iv. The retort is thoroughly purged with nitrogen to expel all traces of air which would otherwise lead to a potential explosive hazard on releasing hydrogen into the system.

v. The cracker gas is admitted into the retort in place of the nitrogen.

iv. The furnace heaters are switched on and the retort rises to a preset maximum temperature. For cast iron and marine based composite wrought iron, a temperature of 850°C has been found to be satisfactory. For land based wrought iron, a lower temperature of 380°C is used. The heating rate is selected such that the maximum operating temperature is reached as soon as possible without causing thermal shock. Typically, the time required to reach 850°C is 20 hours.

vii. After 100 hours, the cracked ammonia is replaced by nitrogen and the furnace allowed to cool to room temperature over a 48 hour period.

viii. The artifacts are removed from the retort and coated either with a low viscosity two pack epoxy varnish or a low bake vinyl lacquer. This surface finish is applied either by vacuum impregnation for small objects or manually for large ones.

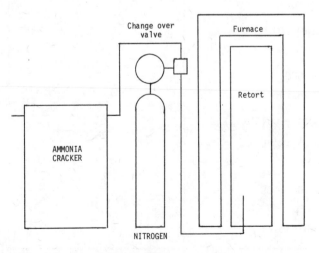

Fig. 19. Schematic diagram of a hydrogen reduction furnace.

The operational conditions stated above have been derived from practical experience gained in continual use of the plant. The aim of the current research is to optimise the operating parameters by studying the reactions occurring within the furnace and the effect of the hydrogen reduction on the metallurgical structure of the artifact. The present paper outlines the initial results obtained in this research programme.

Analysis of the gases issuing from the retort

Analysis of corrosion products from artifacts recovered from marine sites, has shown that the main salts present are $FeOOH$, Fe_3O_4, $FeCl_2$, $FeCl_3$ and FeS together with $NaCl$. The sulphur content was found to vary between 0.6 – 1.75 % by wt while the chloride content ranged from 4.7 – 6.3% by wt (Slade, 1978; Lowther, 1979). The importance of the complete removal of the latter species from the corrosion products is due to the deliquescent nature of the various chloride containing compounds as shown in Table 4. Thus, if the relative humidity of the atmosphere in which the items are stored or displayed, rises above approximately 50% relative humidity, an electrolyte will be present on the metal surface and corrosion will take place. Corrosion will be further accelerated due to the chloride ion increasing the conductivity of the moisture film and its potentiality for destroying any protective passive oxide films which may have been previously formed on the metal surface.

For any conservation treatment to be successful, all traces of chloride must be eliminated and monitoring of the effluent gas from the retort will give a

Salt in Solution	R.H. %
$FeSO_4 \cdot 7H_2O$	92
$(NH_4)_2SO_4$	81
$NaCl$	76
$FeCl_2$	56
$MgCl_2 \cdot 6H_2O$	34
$CaCl_2 \cdot 6H_2O$	32

Table 4. Relative humidities of air in equilibrium with saturated salt solutions at 20°C

good insight into the effectiveness of the hydrogen reduction process in the removal of this troublesome ion.

Samples of the effluent gas were continually withdrawn from a point midway up the retort and a known volume was bubbled through a fixed amount of demineralized water in order to quantify the water soluble portion of the gas. The resultant pH of this solution was measured on a Pye Unicam pH meter (Model PW 9418). The chloride content of the water soluble portion of the effluent gas, was determined gravimetrically by the silver nitrate method (Vogel, 1978). To distinguish between the chloride and sulphide ions, 0.1M copper (II) nitrate was added. Any sulphide present would immediately precipitate out as copper sulphide whilst the copper chloride remains in the solution.

The water insoluble gases in the effluent were

Gas	Range	Reaction and Colour Change	Interferences
HCl	1 - 100 p.p.m.	HCl + bromophenol blue indicator blue → yellow	Cl_2, H_2O, (if ≥ 80% R.H.)
H_2S	1 - 200 p.p.m.	$H_2S + Pb^{2+} \rightarrow PbS + 2H^+$ white pale brown	SO_2
CO_2	0.01 - 1.0 %	$CO_2 + N_2H_4 \rightarrow NH_2 \cdot NH \cdot COOH$	NIL
CO	1 - 1000 p.p.m.	$5CO + I_2O_5 \rightarrow I_2 + 5CO_2$ white brown/violet	C_2H_2, C_6H_6, H_2, H_2S, etc.
Mercaptans	2 - 100 p.p.m.	$C_2H_5SH + Ca(II)$ cpd $\rightarrow Cu(SC_2H_5)_2$ $Cu(SC_2H_5)_2 + S \rightarrow$ yellow/brown Cu cpd pale yellow	H_2S, NH_3, amines
CH_4	Qualitative	$CH_4 + MnO_4^- + H_2S_2O_7 \rightarrow CO$ $CO + I_2O_5 \rightarrow I_2 + CO_2$ white brown/violet	CO, etc.

Table 5. Dräger tube reactions

analysed by means of Dräger tubes. These operate by passing the gas through the tubes packed with the relevant indicator material. A reaction takes place between the specific gas and the constituents to produce a coloured product. The length of the colouration in the tube determines the extent of the reaction and, therefore, the amount of gas present in the effluent. The gases analysed by this method were hydrochloric acid, hydrogen sulphide, carbon monoxide, carbon dioxide, mercaptans and methane. The indicators and reactions occurring within each tube are given in Table 5.

Results

Fig.20 shows the results obtained during the conservation of a cannon recovered from a marine site. The treatment given to the artifact was as outlined above except that the heating cycle was interrupted at 300°C. The retort was maintained at this temperature for 20 hours when the heating cycle was recommenced until the maximum of 850°C was attained

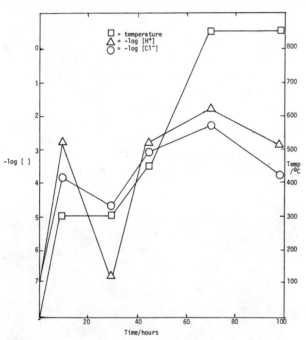

Fig. 20. Analysis of the water soluble products from the reduction of a cannon from a marine site.

and held constant at this value until 100 hours had elapsed. The actual heating rate employed for this cannon was slower than that mentioned above to avoid any risk of thermal damage to the cannon.

From Fig.20 it is evident that the pH of the solution decreased from 7 to 2.7 as the temperature of the retort was gradually raised to 300°C. This corresponds to the evolution of hydrochloric acid from the cannon. The pH slowly increased during the period when the retort was held at this constant temperature and reached pH 7 after 20 hours which indicates that no hydrochloric acid was being produced at this stage. On restarting the heating cycle, the pH decreased again until a minimum of 1.8 was

observed when the temperature reached 850°C. The pH gradually increased to 2.7 at the end of the treatment process.

The chloride content of the water soluble gas parallels the pH as is apparent from Fig.20. The chloride content is expressed as minus logarithm of the molar concentration so as to be consistent with pH values (−logarithm of hydrogen ion concentration).

Analysis of the effluent gas by means of the Dräger tubes gave a similar pattern to that already described as is shown in Table 6. The hydrogen chloride content of the gas phase quickly rose above the maximum detectable limit of the technique used and only fell to measurable levels when the retort was held at 300°C for 20 hours. The value obtained at this point was 6 p.p.m. which is consistent with the pH value of 7 and low chloride content found on analysis of the water soluble gas content at a similar stage of the reduction process. The results recorded for hydrogen sulphide, carbon monoxide and carbon dioxide show the same trend with the concentration initially increasing with rise in retort temperature, a steady decline while the retort was held at 300°C and rising once again when the temperature was raised to a maximum of 850°C.

Temp.	HC1/ppm	H_2S/ppm	CO/ppm	CO_2/ppm
20	0	0	0	0
300	>100	>100	750	9000
300	6	6	100	500
500	>100	50	800	400
850	>100	>100	>1000	>10000

Table 6. Results from Dräger tube analyses

Discussion

The variation of pH and chloride content of the water soluble gases with temperature, has been repeated during the hydrogen reduction of other marine artifacts with the shape of the various graphs being virtually identical in every instance.

The only difference between runs being the actual value of each of the parameters. This is due, in the main, to the extent of corrosion of the original artifact and the porosity of the rust film.

The close agreement between the values of pH and chloride content indicate that the main water soluble constituent of the effluent gas is hydrogen chloride. As the temperature is slowly raised, the physically held water is removed followed by the water of crystallization. When the temperature approaches 300°C, the ferric chloride content of the corrosion products commence to sublime off. (Boiling point of $FeCl_3$ is 294°C.) These gaseous iron salts react with the cracker gas to give hydrogen chloride and 'gaseous' iron according to the following equation:–

$$\tfrac{3}{2}H_{2(g)} + FeCl_{2(g)} \rightarrow Fe_{(g)} + 3HCl_{(g)} \qquad \underline{\hspace{1cm}}(11)$$

Since gaseous iron cannot exist at this low temperature, it deposits on the nearest available sites. This results in the formation of iron needles and these are readily observed when the artifacts are removed from the retort at the end of the treatment process. The hydrogen chloride is swept out of the retort and dissolves in the demineralized water. The amount of sublimation decreases with time at a constant temperature of 300°C until this reaction is virtually exhausted. As the temperature is slowly raised to the maximum of 850°C, the quantity of hydrogen chloride progressively increases. This increase is thought to be due to deeply buried iron chlorides within the corrosion products requiring extra heat in order to remove them from these sites. In addition, the reduction of the oxides of iron will assist in the freeing of the iron chlorides from their entrapment. Subsequent experiments have suggested that very little sodium chloride will sublime off at this temperature and the reducing atmosphere present within the retort while in operation.

The carbon monoxide and dioxide could be produced by the decomposition of any carbonates associated with the rust on the artifacts and/or with the traces of organic material contained within the bore of the cannon (e.g. tar). These could also account for the presence of mercaptans and hydrogen sulphide in the effluent gas though the latter could arise from the presence of iron sulphide in the corrosion product.

Metallurgical effects

The effect of the hydrogen reduction process at 400°C on the microstructure of typical ferrous artifacts was studied. This was investigated by cutting a small section from the object, mounting in a cold setting resin polishing down to $0.25\mu m$ diamond finish and etching in 2% nital solution. The microstructure was examined and photographed using both optical and scanning electron microscopy techniques. Chemical analysis of specific areas of the sample such as inclusions, slag particles, etc., was carried out by use of an electron probe microanalysis facility coupled to the scanning electron microscope.

The sample was cut out from the resin and placed in the retort alongside archaeological artifacts undergoing hydrogen reduction. On completion, the samples were removed and, without any subsequent treatment, re-examined using the two different microscopes. This allowed the same area to be photographed before and after conservation.

As expected, a wide variety of microstuctures were observed even within a small distance along each sample. The predominant microstructure examined consisted of grains of pure ferrite with non-metallic inclusions (Fig.21). No grain growth or

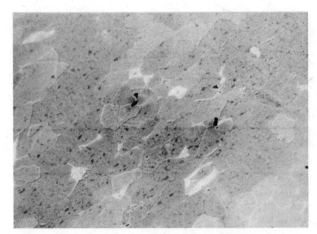

Fig. 21. Scanning electron micrograph of pure ferrite grains with non-metallic inclusions.

recrystallization was noted on these structures after the hydrogen reduction treatment. The inclusion remained unaffected and the chemical analysis of these areas was unaltered by the process.

Another common microstructure associated with artifacts, was the two phase structure of the ferrite plus pearlite. The latter phase probably arose due to the diffusion of carbon into the iron during the fabrication of the article. A typical microstructure is shown in Fig.22. On re-examining this type of structure, no change was visible and there was no sign of spheroidizing of the cementite layers within the pearlite nor was there any evidence of graphitization of the cementite. Using the electron scanning microscope, no difference in the distance between alternate layers of ferrite within the pearlite was observed.

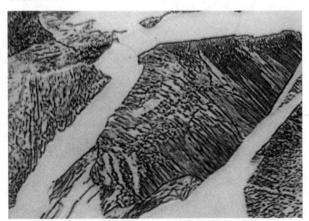

Fig. 22. Scanning electron micrograph of the two phase structure of ferrite plus pearlite.

The most recurrent slag associated with these structures consisted of FeO dendrites in a $2FeO.SiO_2$ eutectic matrix (Fig.23). After exposure to the cracker gas for 100 hours, the two separate phases within the slag were not discernible. This was thought to be due to the reduction of the iron oxides on the surface of the sample by the hydrogen gas. On removal of a few microns from the surface by mechanical polishing using diamond paste, the

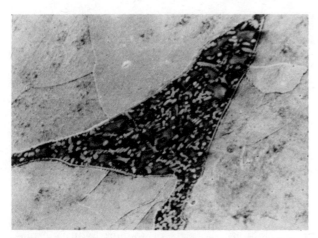

Fig. 23. Scanning electron micrograph of a non-metallic inclusion showing FeO dendrites in a 2FeO.SiO₂ matrix.

structure was again revealed and the chemical composition of the slag remained the same as that determined prior to the conservation process being carried out.

Conclusions

Preliminary results have indicated that a considerable quantity of chloride is removed by hydrogen reduction treatment of ferrous archaeological ob-

jects over a period of 100 hours. This chloride is derived from the sublimation of the ion chlorides which are present in the corrosion products on the surface of the artifacts. Conservation at 400°C causes no change in the microstructure of single phase ferrite or two phase ferrite plus pearlite structures. A slight change was noted when slag particles were re-examined but the original structure could be revealed by simply removing a few microns from the surface of the sample. No alteration in the chemical composition of the metal or slag was detected.

References

Arrhenius, O., Barkman, L. and Sjostrand, E., Conservation of old rusty iron objects. *Swedish Corrosion Institute Bulletin No.61E,* 1973.

Barkman, L., Conservation of rusty iron objects by hydrogen reduction. *Corrosion and Metal Artifacts.* (ed. B.F. Brown *et al*) 1977, pp, 155-166. (NBS Special Publication 479, U.S. Government Printing Office, Washington D.C. 1977).

Lowther, I.R., *Analysis of the Corrosion Products on an Iron Gun Swivel from the Mary Rose.* B.Sc. Applied Chemistry Project, Department of Chemistry, Portsmouth Polytechnic, 1979.

Slade, J., *Analysis of the Corrosion Products on a Rudder Pintle from the Mary Rose.* B.Sc. Applied Chemistry Project, Department of Chemistry, Portsmouth Polytechnic, 1978.

Vogel, A. *Quantitative Inorganic Analysis.* 1978, pp.433-435, Longman, London.

AN ASSESSMENT OF LITHIUM HYDROXIDE AND SODIUM HYDROXIDE TREATMENTS FOR ARCHAELOGICAL IRONWORK

D. Watkinson

Introduction

The attempted stabilization of archaeological ironwork, by the removal of chloride corrosion accelerators contained within artifacts, is one of the major problems facing archaeological conservators. All treatment methods currently in use are totally or partially unsatisfactory in their theory of action, mode of application and/or the results they produce.

It has long been accepted that chlorides are one of the chief causes of continued corrosion in archaeological ironwork (Plenderleith and Werner, 1971), although others (Stambolov, undated) place as much emphasis on sulphur containing compounds. As a consequence of this thinking most treatments aim to remove or inhibit chlorides contained within the artifacts. The form of this chloride has been variously suggested as ferric chloride (Plenderleith and Werner, 1971), or as β-FeOOH in areas of active corrosion (Zucci, Morigi and Bertolasi, 1977), and as FeOCl in marine ironwork (North and Pearson, 1977). It has been suggested recently that the chlorides present at the time of excavation are probably in solution within the pores of the corrosion products (Turgoose, this volume).

Treatments for the removal of chlorides can be classified according to their aims and mode of action. Methods using reduction at high temperatures (Rosenberg, 1917; Arrhenius, Barkman and Sjostrand, 1973; Fabech and Trier, 1978) encounter problems of an ethical nature (North, Owens and Pearson, 1976; Tylecote and Black, 1980). Electrolytic and chemical methods are also questionable as they can remove all evidence of an object's original shape. Inhibitive methods, although attractive in theory, are not very successful in practice. The group of treatments generally constituting the washing methods (Wihr, 1975; Bleck, 1976; Fabech and Trier, 1978; North and Pearson, 1978), seem to be the least questionable ethically since the corrosion layers on the artifact are retained and treatment temperature never exceeds 100°C.

North and Pearson (1978), reviewed a number of washing methods including those using lithium hydroxide and sodium hydroxide. Previously they had suggested chlorides in marine iron were present as FeOCl (North and Pearson, 1977) and they proceeded to show that chloride extraction was diffusion controlled and were able to produce a rate equation for the process. Chloride extraction rates for various washing methods, were determined experimentally over short time periods. Some of their results, indicating the duration of treatment, were based on computer models relying upon their previous theoretical work.

The aim of this paper is to compare the extraction efficiencies of both alcoholic lithium hydroxide and aqueous sodium hydroxide with probably the most commonly used treatment relying upon diffusion: repeated boiling of ironwork in changes of distilled or de-ionised water. The reported post-treatment inhibitive properties of lithium hydroxide/carbonate (Bresle 1974a) have also been investigated, as were similar inhibitive effects of sodium hydroxide/carbonate due to their chemical similarity to lithium hydroxide. All experiments were carried out on terrestrial archaeological ironwork.

For the purposes of this paper, aqueous boiling to remove chloride is taken to be 100% efficient. Of course, this is never the case but this assumption provides a useful datum against which to measure the efficiency of other methods. Currently no one treatment method is suitable for all archaeological ironwork. It is hoped to provide information which will enable conservators to make a more informed choice of treatment method. Similar comparative work for other washing methods will be carried out in the future.

Theoretical background

The lithium hydroxide treatment was first proposed by R. Ake-Bresle in his patent published in 1974 (Bresle, 1974a). In this he summaries the corrosion of ironwork and advocates the use of a lithium hydroxide solution to stabilize archaeological ironwork, by the removal of chlorides, and by the inhibition of further corrosion. Much of his experimental work was on modern steel surfaces which were not extensively corroded (Bresle, 1974a; 1976) as are achaeological iron objects. Fabech and Trier (1978) reported 'good results' when treating archaeological ironwork using lithium hydroxide but gave no details of the quantity of chloride extracted or of post-treatment stability. Thus extensive experimental work on archaelogical ironwork is required to substantiate Bresle's claims for the success of lithium hydroxide.

The recommended treatment procedure is to immerse the ironwork in a solution of lithium hydroxide in an organic solvent. The treatment is claimed to be twofold in its action.

First, chlorides within the artifact react with lithium hydroxide to form lithium chloride which has a high degree of solubility in alcohols and other organic solvents. Thus the chlorides are drawn into solution.

$$LiOH + Cl^- \rightarrow LiCl + OH^- \underline{\quad\quad}(12)$$

28

Second, the object is removed from the treatment solution and air dried. Any residual lithium hydroxide converts to lithium carbonate due to reaction with atmospheric carbon dioxide. This carbonate is contained on and within the object and its corrosion products. As explained by Bresle (1974a), 'An alkaline environment has now been created close to the metal surface, and the increased pH value will passivate the steel surface so as any further rusting is prevented or reduced'.

Apart from the supposed inhibitive properties of the carbonate, the alcoholic lithium hydroxide method seems to have a number of advantages over other washing methods. It is non-aqueous and consequently there should be little or no corrosion of the ironwork during treatment; it requires little attention during treatment and the initial cost of materials is fairly low. Besides the removal of chlorides Bresle (1974a), claims that 'sulphur dioxide and sulphur compounds will be washed away' due to the solubility of these compounds in alcohols.

Weighed against these possible advantages is one obvious disadvantage. The lithium chloride formed during treatment is hygroscopic and forms a solution at relative humidities as low as 15% (Evans, 1972). Any residual lithium chloride contained on or in the iron after treatment would therefore be in solution in almost any storage environment and thus available to stimulate further corrosion.

However, it is unlikely that this would be a serious problem. The quantity of lithium chloride carried over from the treatment solution would probably be very small. Bresle (1974b) claims that no significant amounts of lithium chloride were detectable on the ironwork following treatment. Since other chlorides remaining in the ironwork are hygroscopic anyway then a small residue of lithium chloride should not markedly increase the instability of the object. It is worth noting that it would appear that sodium hydroxide/chloride are soluble enough in alcohol to produce similar reactions to the lithium hydroxide/alcohol solution.

Before going on to discuss the experimental work certain variables need to be considered:–

a. Effect of solvent used on solute concentration

The choice of solvent determines the maximum concentration of lithium hydroxide it is possible to use since its solubility varies according to the alcohol in which it is dissolved (Table 7).

Bresle (1974a), uses a concentration of 0.2% lithium hydroxide in methanol, Fabech and Trier (1978), use 0.2% in a mixture of methanol and isopropanol and North and Pearson (1978), use 0.4% in methanol.

	ETHANOL gl^{-1}	METHANOL gl^{-1}
LiOH	1.8	4.8
LiCl	40	400
NaOH	136	239
NaCl	14.01	0.65

Table 7. The solubility of lithium and sodium compounds in alcohols (After Fabech and Trier, 1978)

The solvent chosen for lithium hydroxide in these experiments was ethanol; the main advantage over methanol being that the vapour is non-toxic. This restricted the concentration of the solution to approximately $2g\,l^{-1}$, or 0.05M. This concentration should be adequate to allow reactions to reach completion in the treatment solution provided that no more than 175 g of ironwork is treated in 1 litre of lithium hydroxide solution. This assumes that the ironwork contains a maximum of 1% chloride by weight; the extra solubility of lithium hydroxide in methanol $(4g\,l^{-1})$ is thus unnecessary.

Lithium hydroxide itself is caustic and injurious to the skin. It is hygroscopic and inhalation of its vapour should be avoided; its vapour can cause severe stinging and watering of the eyes. If ingested in larger amounts it can cause sodium deficiency in both brain and liver tissue (Neretin, 1958). Both solid and solutions should therefore be treated with due care and attention.

b. Temperature

The temperature of treatment is also important since an elevated temperature will increase the total amount of chloride extracted. North and Pearson (1978) observed this and noted that a temporarily increased treatment temperature can permanently elevate extraction rate. This was attributed to physical changes in the corrosion layers of the ironwork. Heated solutions were not used in the present experimental work. The aim was to produce a relatively inexpensive site treatment technique and this excluded the use of heated alcoholic systems which were dangerous and would require costly apparatus.

c. Agitation of the solution

Stirring the solution would increase the rate of chloride extraction if the concentration gradient in the solution was an important factor. Chlorides may build up due to the absence or inability of natural convection currents to disperse them throughout the solution. North and Pearson (1978) encountered no problems with this provided the weight of solution was ten times that of the object. Fabech and Trier (1978), constantly stirred their treatment solution but did not give reasons for doing so. No stirring was employed in any of the experiments described in this paper.

d. Volume of solution

Since diffusion and convection within the solution is relied upon to de-localise chlorides the weight of the ironwork (g) is compared to the volume of the treatment solution (cm³). North and Pearson (1978) suggested a ratio of 1:10 or greater with a change of solution every ten days. Smaller weight to volume ratios than those used by North and Pearson and the effect of less frequent changes of solution per treatment are examined in the present paper. Smaller solution volumes and less frequent changes of solution would reduce the costs incurred when a relatively expensive solvent such as ethanol is used.

e. Immersion time

Factors which increase chloride extraction rate reduce treatment time but do not necessarily increase the absolute quantity of chloride extracted. Bresle (1974a; 1976) mentions treatment times in lithium hydroxide solutions of a 'few minutes' and 'ten minutes' but adds, 'if the rust layer is thick it may be desired to treat the object for a few hours'. Elsewhere, Fabech and Trier (1978) mention immersion periods of several weeks to several months. North and Pearson (1978) used their own equations and calculations to produce a computer model for a hypothetical object containing 10% chloride by weight. They determined that it would take seventeen years for the chloride level in the object to drop to 200 ppm. This assumes that treatment reaches completion. Such long immersion times are clearly unacceptable and would be detrimental to the ironwork.

Each extraction method has the capacity to extract certain quantitities of chloride from ironwork. For the purposes of this paper, when extraction slowed to a point where further removal of significant amounts of chloride would take many months or even years, the treatment was deemed to be complete. The extrapolation of this slow extraction rate would provide information on how long it would take to extract further small quantities of chloride. It could then be determined whether long immersion periods were justified.

f. Archaeological ironwork used in the experiments

The extent of mineralisation in any one archaeological iron object often has to be guessed or the results of an X-radiograph relied upon. This presents problems when attempting to obtain matched samples for experiments. The method of selecting ironwork for the experiments is described below.

Sample material consisted of approximately 100 g batches of roughly equal numbers of objects from several archaeological sites (Table 8). As far as possible objects were selected without regard to precise location on any one site, or to their degree of mineralisation. Work on the extent of object mineralisation as related to its chloride content will be published elsewhere. The ironwork was not cleaned, in order to conform to the requirements of a field treatment.

Chloride extraction using lithium hydroxide and sodium hydroxide

The aims of these experiments were:–

a. To determine the amount of chloride removed from any one batch of ironwork by lithium hydroxide as a percentage of that chloride which would have been removed by aqueous boiling alone.

b. To determine the immersion time required for the optimum removal of chlorides.

c. To investigate the efficiency of ethanol alone as a chloride extractor. This is a control experiment to ensure that the washing action of ethanol is not equal to the action of a lithium hydroxide/ethanol solution.

d. To determine how the sample weight (g) to volume of treatment solution (cm³) ratio affects the rate and quantity of chloride extracted.

e. To investigate the efficiency of aqueous sodium hydroxide as a chloride extractor using the same experimental procedure as that used for lithium hydroxide.

SITE	PERIOD	DATE EXCAVATED	STORAGE CONDITIONS
Swansea	Medieval	1977	Plastic bags only
Dinorben	Iron Age	1977	Cardboard boxes
York	Viking	1976/7/8 1967	Good, silica gel
Breiddin	Iron Age	1975	Good, silica gel
Caerleon	Roman	1978	Good, silica gel
Beeston	17th century	1976	Paper bags
Margam	18th century	1977	Paper bags

Table 8. Archaeological ironwork used in the experiments: provenance, period and storage.

f. To determine the rate of chloride extraction and the overall percentage of chloride extracted.

The longterm stability of the ironwork following treatment was not investigated since it was accepted that some chlorides would remain in the object.

Experimental work

In preliminary experiments the effect of using different volumes of lithium hydroxide solution and of using ethanol only as a chloride extractor were investigated.

Six batches of ironwork were placed in 0.05M lithium hydroxide solution in ethanol. Each sample was placed in a different volume of solution in an individual polythene container with airtight lid. These were used to prevent the hydroxide converting to the ethanol insoluble lithium carbonate by reaction with the ambient air and also to prevent the ethanol absorbing moisture from the atmosphere and thus increasing the possibility of corrosion of the ironwork during treatment. Six control batches were treated similarly in ethanol only. All twelve batches had different sample weight to volume ratios within the range of 1:4 to 1:9.

The chloride content of the solution was measured at regular intervals. The chloride extracted from each batch was related to the weight of ironwork in the batch to determine the value of the ratio:–

$$\frac{\text{Total weight of Cl}^- \text{ extracted at time } t=x\ (\mu g)}{\text{Weight of objects in treatment batch(g)}} = \begin{array}{l}\text{ppm chloride extracted} \\ \text{from the ironwork (at } t=x)\end{array}$$

When no further significant extraction of chloride was recorded the process was deemed to be complete and the treatment terminated. In some cases extended immersion times were used in conjunction with several changes of solution at intervals of 8-14 days.

When treatment of a batch was terminated, the ironwork was boiled in changes of deionised water until consistently low readings of chloride in the wash solution were obtained. The total chloride which it was assumed would be removed by boiling alone was calculated as:–

$$\begin{array}{l}\text{Weight of chloride} \\ \text{removed by} \\ \text{treatment method} \\ \text{(LiOH solution or} \\ \text{ethanol only)}\end{array} + \begin{array}{l}\text{Weight of chloride} \\ \text{removed by} \\ \text{post-treatment} \\ \text{boiling}\end{array} = \begin{array}{l}\text{Total weight of} \\ \text{chloride removed by} \\ \text{aqueous boiling} \\ \text{alone}\end{array}$$

The weight of chloride extracted by lithium hydroxide was then represented as a percentage of this figure. Thus the efficiency of lithium hydroxide as compared to a standard aqueous boiling technique could be determined.

Results and Discussion

Reactions in the lithium hydroxide solution sometimes produced a thick precipitate of ferric hydroxide. The presence or absence of precipitate could not be related to either a high chloride content in the ironwork or to a more efficient removal of chlorides by the solution. Generally, ferric ions were present in the treatment solution whether it was ethanol alone or lithium hydroxide, as evidenced by the rust colouration of the solution. On removal from the treatment bath and after air drying, all the objects treated in lithium hydroxide solution showed traces of a white powder on their surface, thought to be lithium carbonate.

Variation of the sample weight to volume ratio within the region 1:4 to 1:9 w/v, does not seem to affect the overall percentage of chloride removed by the solution (Fig.24) and there is no indication that chloride extraction is improved by larger volumes of solution. Taking these results into consideration a

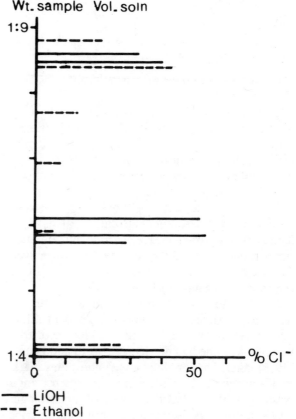

Fig. 24. Varience of the percentage chloride extracted (Cl⁻ extracted by treatment + boiling + 100%) with the sample weight (g) to volume of solution (cm³) ratio.

weight to volume ratio of 1:6 was chosen for the remainder of the experiments, including those in which aqueous sodium hydroxide was used.

The treatments using ethanol alone extracted a lower percentage of chloride than equivalent treatments using lithium hydroxide solutions (Fig.25). On average ethanol alone was approximately half as efficient as lithium hydroxide solution. The mean percentage chloride extracted from the six lithium hydroxide batches was 37% and the mean for the six ethanol batches, 20%. The extraction of chlorides in a lithium hydroxide/ethanol solution must be due, in some part, to the action of the lithium hydroxide.

31

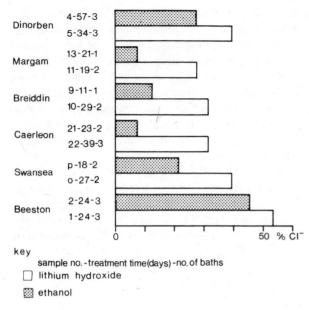

key
        sample no.-treatment time(days)-no.of baths
        ☐ lithium hydroxide
        ▨ ethanol

Fig. 25. Amount of chloride extracted with lithium hydroxide solution as compared to that extracted with ethanol alone.

None of these solutions were as efficient as aqueous boiling of the ironwork.

Extraction rate of chlorides seemed to be faster during the first 1-5 days and then slowed markedly with time. All experiments were terminated when the extraction of chlorides appeared to have stopped or was minimal. Long immersion times did not seem to extract a greater percentage of chloride.

Comparing the efficiency of two preparatory lithium hydroxide solutions, Breidden 10 and Caerleon 22, each extracted 31% chloride but immersion times varied, being 29 days and 39 days respectively. The treatment baths were changed every 10 to 15 days and this seemed adequate.

Fig. 26 shows the chloride extraction rates of a number of batches of ironwork treated in lithium hydroxide. Most samples had one change of treatment bath; some had no change. North and Pearson (1978) state that for short immersion times marine cast iron shows a chloride extraction rate $\propto t^{\frac{1}{2}}$ for all washing methods. For the terrestrial archaeological wrought ironwork used in the experiments described here it only appears to be true for 1-3 days ($t^{\frac{1}{2}} = 5{\rightarrow}8.5h^{\frac{1}{2}}$); after this period the extraction rate begins to slow down considerably. By extrapolation of the rate curve beyond 40 days ($t^{\frac{1}{2}} = 31h^{\frac{1}{2}}$) it can be seen that a further nine months immersion would only produce a small increase in the percentage of chloride extracted, perhaps 5%-15% depending upon the quantity of chloride in the object.

North and Pearson (1978), when plotting chloride extracted against $t^{\frac{1}{2}}$, observed that the linearity of the chloride extraction rate was maintained until, '85% of the initial chloride has been removed'.

The linearity of the extraction rates in the lithium hydroxide experiments described here, were constant for the removal of 55% – 70% of the chloride

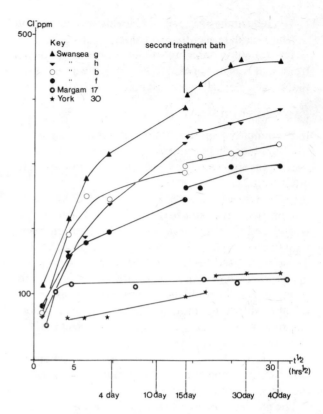

Fig. 26. Chloride extracted against $t^{\frac{1}{2}}$ for six different samples treated in lithium hydroxide solution.

which was removed by t = 40 days. Longer treatment times would reduce this percentage as further small amounts of chloride would be extracted. This short linearity could be due to the fact that terrestrial ironwork contains less chloride than marine ironwork. Also the ironwork used by North and Pearson was cast iron not wrought iron, as was used in these experiments. Cast iron has a different composition and structure to wrought iron and consequently the structure and porosity of corroded wrought and cast iron objects will differ, which could lead to a different rate of chloride release.

Long immersion times are undesirable as the presence of hydroxides and high pH media can result in lamination of rust layers, consequent weakening of the object and loss of shape. This is more pronounced in an aqueous medium such as aqueous sodium hydroxide although ethanol, which was used as the solvent in the lithium hydroxide treatment, may absorb moisture from the atmosphere leading to further corrosion of the iron immersed in the bath.

Extraction rates for the lithium hydroxide treatment were compared by examining the chloride extracted at different values of $t^{\frac{1}{2}}$.

The percentage of chloride extracted by any one lithium hydroxide treatment at any chosen value of t is recorded in Table 9. The chloride extracted by lithium hydroxide at t = 40 days was taken to equal 100% efficiency for each treatment. This was thought permissible since the small amount of chlor-

32

ide extracted by an extended immersion period of one year, as determined by extrapolation, was considered negligible. Allowing for experimental error, these values are fairly similar for each bath of ironwork treated. At t = 30 days ($t^{\frac{1}{2}}$ = 26.8$h^{\frac{1}{2}}$) the extraction rates of chloride for most batches are similar, all being within the region of 93% – 99% complete. Thus it would seem that an immersion time of 30-40 days fulfills the requirement of the treatment almost going to completion. The ironwork should not deteriorate unduly during the 40 day treatment period.

The treatment bath was changed once for most samples. It can be seen from Fig.26 that at the point where the treatment bath is changed there is a small jump in chloride extraction but that the extraction rate beyond this point continues as before. The initial increase in chloride extraction could have been due to a carry over of chlorides from the

Aqueous sodium hydroxide behaved in a similar manner to lithium hydroxide with respect to percentage chloride extracted at given values of time, although aqueous sodium hydroxide tended to have a slightly faster extraction rate than lithium hydroxide. Consequently, similar immersion periods to lithium hydroxide are applicable when using aqueous sodium hydroxide.

Fig.27 shows the percentage chloride removed in seventeen lithium hydroxide and six sodium hydroxide treated batches. The number of times the treatment bath was changed and the immersion time, in days, is also shown.

By comparing the results for the Swansea site it can be seen that sodium hydroxide is more efficient than lithium hydroxide in extracting chloride. The range of chloride extraction for lithium hydroxide was 8% to 62%, with 14 out of 17 samples in the region 25% – 40%, with a mean of 36%.

SAMPLE NUMBER AND SITE	% Cl⁻ EXTRACTED AT t(% Cl⁻ extracted at t = 40days = 100%)				% Cl⁻ extracted in second and final treatment bath t=15 days →t=40 days
	t = 4 days ($t^{\frac{1}{2}}$=9.8$h^{\frac{1}{2}}$)	t = 10 days ($t^{\frac{1}{2}}$=15.5$h^{\frac{1}{2}}$)	t = 14 days ($t^{\frac{1}{2}}$=18.3$h^{\frac{1}{2}}$)	t = 30 days ($t^{\frac{1}{2}}$=26.8$h^{\frac{1}{2}}$)	
SWANSEA A	79%	85%	89%	96%	16%
SWANSEA B	77%	84%	87%	97%	14%
SWANSEA E	68%	79%	85%	98%	14%
SWANSEA F	66%	77%	81%	91%	17%
SWANSEA G	71%	80%	83%	99%	16%
SWANSEA H	63%	77%	84%	95%	14%
					second bath York t=20 days →t=40 days
YORK 1	64%	71%	73%	96%	23%
YORK 3	60%	73%	79%	93%	—
YORK 4	62%	64%	68%	92%	26%
YORK 5	57%	63%	72%	97%	22%

Table 9. Percentage chloride extracted from ironwork at selected time intervals up to 40 days and percentage chloride extracted in the second treatment bath. (Total amount of chloride extracted from t = 0 – t = 40 days = 100%).

chloride contaminated first bath to the uncontaminated second bath. From these observations it was concluded that frequent changing of the immersion solution and long treatment times would not produce either a significantly higher overall extraction of chloride or a faster extraction rate during treatment.

Only six sodium hydroxide batches were tested but five of these extracted at least 10% more chloride than the most efficient lithium hydroxide result and 20% more than the second most efficient result. The mean of the sodium hydroxide results was 72%.

It is worth noting that immersion periods in aqueous sodium hydroxide were short, being only

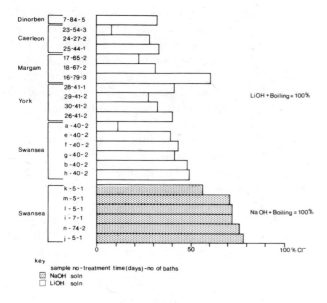

Fig. 27. The percentage of chloride extracted with lithium and sodium hydroxide treatments as compared to aqueous boiling (Cl⁻ extracted by treatment + boiling = 100%).

5-7 days. Immersion periods of longer than this would probably have produced a greater extraction of chloride; thus the mean efficiency of aqueous sodium hydroxide may be closer to 80%.

The efficiencies of lithium hydroxide, sodium hydroxide and ethanol as compared to aqueous boiling can be presented as:–

Boiling	:	Aqueous sodium Hydroxide 0.5M	:	Alcoholic Lithium Hydroxide 0.05M	:	Ethanol
100%	:	72%	:	36%	:	20%

From this it can be seen that on average sodium hydroxide is almost twice as efficient a chloride extractor as lithium hydroxide, but that neither method is as efficient as aqueous boiling.

Inhibitive effects of lithium and sodium hydroxide treatments
Introduction and theory

Lithium and sodium hydroxides will convert to their carbonates in air:–

$$2LiOH + CO_2 \rightarrow Li_2CO_3 + H_2O \quad \text{————(13)}$$
$$2NaOH + CO_2 \rightarrow Na_2CO_3 + H_2O \quad \text{————(14)}$$

Both of these carbonates are soluble in water, producing an alkaline environment (Table 10).

Carbonates of many varieties have been used to inhibit corrosion in various environments. Lithium and sodium carbonate are both thought to act as alkaline inhibitors although there is some dispute regarding their mode of action. One possibility is

	Cold water (gl⁻¹)	Hot water (gl⁻¹)	pH sat soln
Li_2CO_3	15.4	7.2	11.7
$Na_2CO_3 \cdot 1H_2O$	71.0	455.5	11.9

Table 10. Solubilities of lithium and sodium carbonates in hot and cold water and the pH of these solutions.

that they may inhibit corrosion by forming an alkaline environment in oxygenated waters:–

$$2Na^+ + CO_3^{2-} + 2H_2O \rightarrow H_2CO_3 + 2Na^+ + 2OH^- \text{————(15)}$$

weak acid   strong base

(after Abbot, 1965)

Provided the concentration of sodium carbonate is high enough, it will form a solution of approximately pH 11.9 in water. This pH is continuously maintained by the sodium carbonate as a buffer. As hydroxide is removed the equation tends towards the right. In the case of ordinary alkaline inhibitors, as hydroxide ions are used up, they are not replaced.

An alternative to this theory is mentioned by Stambolov (undated). He states that at a pH greater than 8.4 hydroxyl ions, which are produced at cathodic sites when ferric ions enter solution from anodic sites on the metal surface will increase pH at the metal-solution boundary. The carbonates present in the solution will then precipitate and when mixed with the ion hydroxides will create a compact protective layer on the iron surface preventing further corrosion.

Alkaline carbonate inhibitors probably work by a mixture of the above theories. However, chloride ions or other corrosion accelerators can break down the protective thin adherent oxide film on the metal surface intensifying localised attack and pitting. Chlorides will almost certainly be present on archaeological iron objects following any washing method.

A second point against an alkaline type inhibitor working successfully is that thick corrosion layers interfere with access of hydroxide ions to the metal surface where the inhibition must take place. Almost all archaeological iron objects have thick corrosion layers which it is necessary to retain in order to preserve the shape of the object.

For alkaline inhibitors to function they must be in solution. This means that the ambient R.H. must be high enough for the slightly hygroscopic carbonate powders to attract enough moisture for a solution of carbonates to be formed next to the metal surface and within the porous corrosion layers on archaelogical ironwork. It would seem unlikely that ambient R.H. would be sufficiently high to do this.

Also the concentration of hydroxide and carbonate carried from the treatment solution, on and within the object, must be sufficient to produce these solutions on the object surface. They must also be evenly distributed to enable an overall inhibitive effect to take place.

34

The concentration of lithium carbonate solution required to inhibit the corrosion of uncorroded wrought iron billets, weighing from 1 to 2g was established. The billets were placed in individual glass beakers containing 25cm^3 of test solution. The upper surface was in a well aerated solution whereas the underside rested on the bottom of the beaker and was therefore in a low oxygen environment. Two types of corrosion could be expected; a black magnetite on the oxygen starved areas and orange/yellow/green coloured oxides on the oxygen rich surfaces. Corrosion or non-corrosion was determined by the appearance of corrosion products either on the metal billet or in solution. The results in Table 11 show that a 2500 ppm solution of lithium carbonate is required before corrosion is inhibited to any degree.

The effect of chlorides on the inhibitive properties of lithium and sodium carbonate was tested. Fresh wrought iron samples, as described above, were immersed in carbonate solutions containing chloride ions. The criteria used for determining corrosion was the same as that used previously. The results are shown in Table 12.

The presence of chlorides in concentrations of 76 ppm or greater nullified any inhibitive effects of either sodium or lithium carbonate at the concentrations examined.

The inhibitive effects of carbonate residues on archaeological ironwork, previously boiled to remove as much chloride as possible, were examined. One batch of ironwork was soaked in either 0.5M or 0.07M aqueous lithium carbonate solution and another batch soaked in either 0.5M or 0.07M aqueous sodium carbonate. The objects were then allowed to air dry. This would simulate the residues that might be expected on the surface of ironwork following treatment by lithium or sodium hydroxide solutions.

CONCENTRATION Li$_2$CO$_3$ (ppm)	IMMERSION TIME		
	16 HOURS	91 HOURS	69 DAYS
10	$\frac{7}{8}$ surface ferric corrison	whole surface ferric corrosion	whole sample corroded and ptt. in solution
100	$\frac{7}{8}$ surface ferric corrosion	whole surface ferric corrosion	whole sample corroded and ptt. in solution
250	$\frac{1}{8}$ surface ferric corrosion	whole surface ferric corrosion	whole sample corroded and ptt. in solution
1000	small spot ferric corrosion	ferric corrosion on underside	whole sample corroded and ptt. in solution
2500	none	none	corrosion on underside
5000	none	none	none
SAT. SOLN	none	none	none
CONTROL WATER ONLY	whole surface ferric corrosion	——————	——————

Table 11. The inhibitive properties of different lithium carbonate solutions

Conc. of Li_2CO_3 (ppm)	Conc. Of Cl^- (ppm)	IMMERSION TIME	
		3 days	63 days
2500	76	none	extensive local corrosion underside corrosion
2500	76	none	extensive local corrosion underside corrosion
2500	305	none	extensive local corrosion underside corrosion
2500	305	slight local corr	extensive local corrosion underside corrosion
5000	76	none	none
5000	76	none	slight corrosion
5000	305	none	extensive local corrosion underside corrosion
5000	305	none	extensive local corr underside corrosion
Control (water only)	76	extensive overall corrosion $\longrightarrow$	
Control (water only)	305	extensive overall corrosion $\longrightarrow$	
Control (water only)	610	extensive overall corrosion $\longrightarrow$	

Conc. of Na_2CO_3 (ppm)	Conc. of Cl^- (ppm)	IMMERSION TIME	
		3 days	162 days
7420	nil	none	none
7420	nil	none	overall corrosion
7420	76	none	overall corrosion
7420	76	local corrosion	local corrosion
7420	305	slight local corrosion	extensive local corrosion
7420	305	slight local corrosion	extensive local corrosion
5300	nil	slight local corrosion	$\longrightarrow$
5300	nil	underside corrosion	$\longrightarrow$
5300	76	slight local corrosion	underside corrosion
5300	76	slight local corrosion	underside corrosion
5300	305	underside corrosion	extensive local corrosion
5300	305	underside corrosion	extensive local corrosion

Table 12. Effect of chlorides on the inhibitive properties of lithium and sodium carbonate at selected concentrations.

One group of carbonate treated objects was then impregnated with microcrystaline wax and subjected to a relative humidity of approximately 80% for differing periods of time. This RH should be sufficient for a carbonate solution to form on the object surface. Corrosion was deemed to be taking place in mined by the release of chloride and of carbonate from the object, controlled corrosion.

The carbonate pre-treatment did not govern corrosion of the samples subjected to high relative humidity, nor did waxing or non-waxing of the objects. Some control samples, impregnated with

PRETREATMENT SOLUTION	SAMPLE WEIGHT (g)	SAMPLE CROSS SECTION	IMMERSION TIME	
			3 days	30 days
$0.5M\ Li_2CO_3$	7.8	mineralised	none	none
	7.0	mineralised	none	none
$0.5M\ Na_2CO_3$	5.2	Fe core	corrosion	corrosion
	4.5	Fe core	corrosion	corrosion
$0.07M\ Li_2CO_3$	3.7	Fe core	corrosion	corrosion
	4.6	Fe core	none	corrosion
$0.07M\ Na_2CO_3$	2.9	Fe core	none	corrosion
	18.3	Fe core	corrosion	corrosion
CONTROLS	5.0	Fe core	corrosion	corrosion
BOILED	7.7	Fe core	corrosion	corrosion
OBJECT	8.1	mineralised	none	none
IMPREGNATED	9.3	mineralised	none	none
WITH WAX	18.5	mineralised	none	none

Table 13. Corrosion samples impregnated with carbonates and wax and then subjected to a high relative humidity (80%)

these objects if pustules of wet ferric corrosion and/or lamination of the object was visible (Table 13).

A second group of carbonate impregnated ironwork was placed in individual beakers containing $75cm^3$ of de-ionised water. If the solution showed signs of coloration due to ferric ions or a ferric precipitate, it was presumed that corrosion was taking place. The pH of the solutions was recorded. The chloride content of each solution was monitored to determine how much chloride was being released from the ironwork (Table 14).

Results from both tests were inconclusive. There was no common factor linking carbonate pre-treatment with corrosion when samples were immersed in water since some control samples corroded and others did not. Neither the chloride concentration nor the pH of the solution, as deter-

carbonate but unwaxed, did not corrode whilst others, similarly treated, did corrode. Similarly, some waxed objects pre-treated with carbonate corroded, others did not.

What factor was governing corrosion? It was thought that the extent of corrosion in the artifact itself might be governing corrosion. Each object used in these experiments was broken into two and its cross section examined to determine the extent of its corrosion. They were classified into three categories:–

i. Solid metal core surrounded by corrosion (the core may have been only a slither of metal but this still placed the object in this category).

ii. Total mineralisation, solid cross section.

iii. Total mineralisation, void in the centre of the object.

PRETREATMENT SOLUTION	SAMPLE WEIGHT (g)	SAMPLE CROSS SECTION	IMMERSION TIME		pH of SOLN (t=30)	TOTAL Cl$^-$ IN SOLN(μg) WEIGHT OBJECT (g)
			3 days	30 days		
O.5M Li$_2$CO$_3$	4.3	mineralised	corrosion	corrosion	8.7	61
	18.5	Fe core	none	corrosion	8.3	467
	7.4	Fe core	corrosion	corrosion	9.3	228
0.5M Na$_2$CO$_3$	3.4	Fe core	corrosion	corrosion	8.3	163
	7.9	mineralised	none	none	9.3	28
	6.7	Fe core	corrosion	corrosion	8.9	32
O.07M Li$_2$CO$_3$	9.7	Fe core	corr	corrosion	7.5	46
	13.7	mineralised	none	none	9.1	29
	5.2	mineralised	none	none	8.5	38
	8.4	mineralised	none	none	9.0	58
	4.5	mineralised	none	none	8.6	60
O.07M Na$_2$CO$_3$	12.6	mineralised	corrosion	corrosion	8.6	95
	9.3	Fe core	corrosion	corrosion	7.5	150
	24.8	Fe core	none	corrosion	7.8	228
CONTROLS NO PRE-TREATMENT	7.1	Fe core	none	corrosion	5.3	44
	7.1	mineralised	none	none	8.1	1509
	22.3	mineralised	none	none	5.1	186
	14.0	mineralised	none	none	6.4	1932
	13.4	mineralised	none	none	8.1	2019
	19.8	mineralised	none	none	8.1	118

Table 14. Corrosion of samples impregnated with carbonates and wax and then immersed in 75cm^3 of deionised water.

For the objects tested by immersion in 75cm³ of de-ionised water the pH of the solution in which they were immersed, the chloride content of that solution and the weight of the object were plotted against the condition of the object (Figs.28, 29 and 30). It can be seen that the object condition controls whether the artifact does or does not corrode. Fig.30 also contains the results of the samples tested in a high

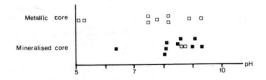

Fig. 28. Corrosion of samples immersed in 75cm³ of de-ionised water as related to the extent of mineralisation and the pH of the solution.

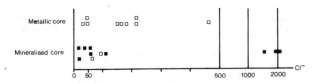

Fig. 29. Corrosion of samples immersed in 75cm³ of de-ionised water as related to the extent of mineralisation and the chloride content of the solution.

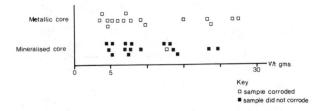

Fig. 30. Corrosion of samples immersed in 75cm³ de-ionised water and those tested in high relative humidity (80%) as related to the extent of mineralisation and the weight of the sample

relative humidity. Ironwork retaining a metal core tends to corrode whereas totally mineralised ironwork does not seem to corrode using the corrosion criteria detailed in this paper. The two samples placed in the totally mineralised category and which did corrode may have contained small traces of metal which were undetected in the cross section of the object.

Conclusions

The treatment time recommended for 0.05M lithium hydroxide and 0.5M sodium hydroxide is approximately 30 to 40 days with one change of the treatment solution at 15 days. This treatment regime should remove approximately 80 to 90% of the chloride which the treatment method is capable of removing from the object within 1 to 2 years immersion. The further amount of chloride removed after 40 days immersion will be dependent on the chloride

content of the object but it is likely that these quantities will be negligible when compared to the bulk of the chloride removed. Also long immersion times may be detrimental to the object, if not chemically, then physically.

The weight of ironwork to volume of treatment solution ratio should be in the region of 1:4 to 1:9. A ratio of 1:6 is considered desirable as the volume of the solution is not then excessive and natural convection currents within the solution appear to maintain the necessary concentration gradients.

When comparing the extraction of chlorides from archaeological wrought ironwork, 0.5M aqueous sodium hydroxide has a greater extraction capacity and is approximately twice as efficient in this respect than is 0.05M alcoholic lithium hydroxide. Repeated aqueous boiling is a more efficient method of chloride extraction than either lithium or sodium hydroxide treatments. No tests with heated hydroxide solutions were carried out as it was thought that hot sodium hydroxide may damage the corrosion layers on the object.

Neither lithium or sodium hydroxide/carbonate residues remaining on the surface of the object following treatment impart any inhibitive properties to the object under the conditions investigated in this paper. Post treatment corrosion would appear to be governed by the condition of the object treated, in that those with a metal core are open to further rapid corrosion whereas those with a totally mineralised structure are not. The decision to use either lithium or sodium hydroxide to treat archaeological ironwork lies with the conservator. Neither is as efficient as aqueous boiling but each has its own advantages and disadvantages. Aqueous boiling can cause damage to the ironwork due to thermal expansion and contraction; it involves much attention by the conservator and long treatment periods at the end of which not all the chlorides are removed and stability cannot be guaranteed. Lithium and sodium hydroxide offer alternative methods with reduced efficiency of chloride extraction. They do however, impose less stress on the ironwork and require the minimum of preparation, attention and cost. Also the possible damage to amphoteric metals associated with the ironwork caused by the alkaline environment during treatment must not be discounted.

In conclusion, none of the three methods mentioned in this paper are suitable for the stabilization of archaeological ironwork. None of them will extract all the chloride from the ironwork. Consequently, objects retaining a metallic core will be left potentially unstable and those which are totally mineralised will probably be no more stable or unstable than they were before treatment. A totally new approach to the stabilization of archaeological ironwork is required. Perhaps this will involve careful environmental control, whether physical and/or chemical, instead of the usual unsuccessful and damaging attempts to remove the chloride corrosion accelerators.

Acknowledgements

My thanks to Dr. Stephen Turgoose, Department of Chemistry, University College, Cardiff for advice and guidance and to my colleague, Dr. David Leigh, for encouragement and discussion throughout the work. The experiments would not have been possible without ironwork kindly provided by Gwent-Glamorgan, Clwyd-Powys and York Archaeological Trusts and by Mr. Peter Hough.

References

Abbot, D., *Inorganic Chemistry*. 1965. London.

Arrhenius, O., Barkman, L. and Sjostrand, E., Conservation of old rusty iron objects. Reduction of rust with hydrogen gas. *Swedish Corrosion Institute Bulletin No.61E*, 1973.

Bleck, R.D., Ein nuer Vorschlag zur Enzalzung archaeologischer Bodenfunde ans Eisen. *Neue Museumkunde. 19* 1976, p.3.

Bresle, S.A., a, A method and a composition for reducing the rusting of articles of iron and steel or ferrous alloys. *British Patent No. 1358 146*, 1974.

Bresle, S.A. b, Nya metoder for konserveriung av antikvariska jarnforemal. *Jernkont. Ann. 158* 1974.

Bresle, S.A., Painting rusty old metal surfaces, a new look at an old problem. *Metal Finishing*. July, 1976.

Evans, U.R., *An Introduction to Metallic Corrosion*. 2nd Ed. 1963. London.

Evans, U.R., *The Rusting of Iron: Causes and Control*. 1972. London.

Fabech, E.W. and Trier, J., Notes on the conservation of iron, especially the red-hot heating and lithium hydroxide methods. *Conservation of Iron Objects Found in Salty Environments*. (ed. R.M. Organ, E.M. Nosek and J. Lehmann) 1978 pp.65-75. (Historical Monuments Documentation Centre, Warsaw).

Neretin, V., Comparative toxicity of some lithium compounds in acute tests on animals. *Farmikol i Toksikol. 21.N* 1958, pp.93-96.

North, N.A., Owens, M. and Pearson, C., Thermal stability of cast and wrought marine iron. *Studies in Conservation 21*. 1976, pp.192-197.

North, N.A. and Pearson, C., Thermal decomposition of FeOCl and marine cast iron corrosion products. *Studies in Conservation. 22* 1977, pp.146-157.

North, N.A. and Pearson, C., Washing methods for chloride removal from marine iron artifacts. *Studies in Conservation. 23* 1978, pp.173-186.

Nosek, E.M., Research and conservation of the iron objects currently displayed at the salt mine museum. *Conservation of Iron Objects Found in Salty Environments*. (ed R.M. Organ, E.M. Nosek and J. Lehmann) 1978, pp.9-20. (Historical Monuments Documentation Centre, Warsaw).

Plenderleith, H.J. and Werner, A.E.A., *The Conservation of Antiquities and Works of Art*. 2nd Ed. 1971. Oxford University Press, London.

Rosenberg, G.A., Antiques en Fer et en Bronze leur transformation dans la verre contenantlacide carbonique et des chlorures et leur Conservation. 1917. Copenhagen.

Stambolov, T., *The Corrosion and Conservation of Metallic Antiquities and Works of Art*. Cultural Research Laboratory for Objects of Art and Science, Amsterdam. (undated).

Tylecote, R.F. and Black, J.W.B. The effect of hydrogen reduction on the properties of ferrous materials. *Studies in Conservation. 25* 1980, pp.87-96.

Wihr, R., Electrolytical desalination of archaeological iron. *Conservation in Archaeology and the Applied Arts*. Stockholm Congress, 1975, pp.189-194.

Zucchi, F., Morigi, G. and Bertolasi, V., Beta iron oxide hydroxide formation in localised active corrosion of iron artifacts. *Corrosion and Metal Artifacts*. (ed. B.F. Brown et al) 1977, pp.103-105. (NBS Special Publication 479, U.S. Government Printing Office, Washington D.C. 1977).

DISCUSSION

Chairman:
J.M. Black

S. Keene

Have you monitored the chloride content of the actual objects that have been processed as well as the chloride content of the gases evolved?

D. Barker

We do monitor the gases but as yet we have not measured the chloride content of the objects. We propose to take core samples of metal from the objects, analyse the chloride concentration through the rust layers then subject the object to the process and repeat the analysis to see how the chloride distribution has altered. It may well be that we are only taking the chlorides from the outer most surface layers and I have no proof that we have removed all the chlorides. But by analysing the gas either by dissolving it in water or by using Dräger tubes we should be able to reach a point when we can say that we have got all the chlorides out.

J. Black

When you have carried out the hydrogen reduction what sort of surface does the object have?

D. Barker

It is fairly porous. After we have conserved the object, we soak it in an epicote resin to prevent further corrosion.

J. Black

What happens if you don't coat with a resin?

C.O'Shea

The object oxidises extremely rapidly.

L. Biek

Do you find the pH of the object is still low, is still acidic, before you put the resin in?

D. Barker

We have no way of telling. As you saw from the figures the pH was falling at the end of the experiment but it's still quite high. That was for a cannon from a marine environment that we treated. When we do the experiments with other objects, we get exactly the same curve but of course the values are different. The problem obviously, is that we have got to continue the process until we have got the chlorides, or the chlorides in the gas phase, down to a fixed value. We do not know that fixed value yet but we hope to find out in the near future.

L. Biek

So at the moment you are still putting in the resin while the object is acidic?

D. Barker

It's only the gas phase that is acidic. What we are doing is destroying the chlorides and they are coming off as a gas which is acidic. The example of the cannon looked as though it still had some chloride in it but some of the other objects we have monitored, the chlorides have come down to very low levels. The process could obviously be continued until we get down to a certain set level and and this is where an accurate analytical method is required so that we can say we have got all the chloride out. It is the chloride that is undoubtedly the problem.

J. Black

How successful do you think the hydrogen reduction method is and why?

C. O'Shea

We have had our failures particularly in the early days, but we can to some extent govern our success by controlling the temperature. We do know that if we raise the temperature of the retort to above 800°C we can guarantee total reduction.

J. Ashley-Smith

It's called the hydrogen reduction method but to what extent are the corrosion products reduced to the metal? Is it reduced or do you remove the corrosion products?

D. Barker

What we can say definitely is that we reduce all the iron chlorides, salts and those corrosion products that will be decomposed easily. Whether we reduce $FeOOH$ and Fe_3O_4 back to the metal, I don't think we can honestly say that does happen. We have investigated some salts but not the actual rust itself.

J. Ashley-Smith

Does the object look metallic when you bring it out of the furnace?

D. Barker

It looks black.

C. O'Shea

I think we are in effect, achieving a certain amount of total reduction but it's the reduction of new iron or reduced or particulate iron. Because in many instances, if you take a partially treated object and give it a gentle brush with a soft wire brush you get a metallic shine; it is almost certainly metal. The process will totally reduce the corrosion products of iron back into iron depending on the temperature you are using and the length of time you subject the object to the treatment. Judging by the amount of steam coming out of the exhaust bore at the higher temperatures, even after 100 hours, and assuming the steam is a product of the reduction we are in fact reducing to metallic iron.

J. Ashley-Smith
How stable is that, are you in fact just getting dust that has fallen off or perhaps pyrophoric iron?

C.O'Shea
We have examples of pyrophodic reactions, disasterous ones, immediately after treatment.

A. David
We heard earlier about the information that could be held in the corrosion layers. With the hydrogen reduction method does the object undergo any mechanical cleaning before treatment to retrieve such information?

C. O'Shea
Yes it does. For instance the large cannon from marine sites are heavily concreted and we treat them more or less as one would treat a piece from a land based archaeological site. This is probably the most time consuming part of the whole process.

S. Keene
Returning to the question of success rate. I have only seen objects from three collections that have been treated by the hydrogen reduction method, but in each case there are clear signs that the object is still unstable. Do you monitor in any way the objects you have treated?

C.O'Shea
It is very difficult because most of the objects which have been treated belong to people whose museums are a considerable distance away and we usually rely on them to come back to us if there is any reoccurrence of the corrosion. The results have been very encouraging so far. We have accounted for the failures that did occur probably because we were treating for too short a time at too low a temperature.

D. Clarke
Are you not concerned that in those treatments you carry out at the higher temperatures that you will be producing an article that is no longer in the same metallurgical condition as it was originally?

D. Barker
Yes we are concerned. The only objects we put into the furnace at the higher temperatures are cast iron objects. The wrought iron ones we put at a temperature limit of 400°C. We have done some work on Saxon blades but it's too early to say whether any change in the structure of these objects has occurred. My paper, to-day, was intended to show that if we take a wrought iron object which has a pearlitic structure around the edge, or some pearlite present, then basically that pearlite will not have altered as a result of the treatment itself.

Anon
You did say that the wrought iron objects from the sea were treated at 850°C?

D. Barker
Yes, because I think there is so much chloride in the marine based objects anyway we would not have driven out all the salt at 400°C. We have probably got rid of all the iron chloride at 400°C, the peak at 300°C is probably the iron chlorides that have been removed, but I do not think we have removed all the salt from the system. That is why if you have marine objects and they are wrought iron and you are not intending to look at the metallographic structure afterwards, then you can treat them at 850°C. We have not done any work on the metallurgical structure at 850°C because we accept that it will alter. We are concerned if there is going to be any change at 400°C. Most of the iron objects we have looked at – such as rudder pintels, Roman nails, some knives with a simple pearlite structure and slags – we have not observed any change at all after 100 hours.

V. Daniels
What do you think is the eventual fate of sodium chloride, is it reduced to sodium hydride?

K. Kendell
At the higher temperatures you will find that although it is not anywhere near its melting or boiling point the sodium chloride does have an appreciable, measureable vapour pressure and since you have a flow system you are continually removing the products of the reaction so you are effectively subliming it off. You can plot a graph which gives a good relationship between temperature and weight loss of sodium chloride. In fact, at local cool spots in the furnace such as gas inlet pipes, you can observe the growth of needle-like crystals of sodium chloride.

D. Leigh
What are the temperature measurements you have been doing in the furnace, particularly above 400°C?

D. Barker

We have three temperature probes in the furnace and the temperature remains fairly constant over the whole length of the retort. The micro-structure I showed was from some Roman nails which were treated in a small muffle furnace where the temperature is much more accurately controlled.

D. Leigh

Is there any evidence of exothermic reactions?

D. Barker

I would not like to say at this stage. We have done some differential thermal analysis investigations but when we pass hydrogen over the corrosion products in the d.t.a. equipment the hydrogen tends to melt the thermocouple; we cannot get above 600°C. We are redesigning the d.t.a. equipment and it is to early yet to make any statement; there is some exothermic reaction going on but to what extent and what temperature rises we will get we cannot say.

A. Oldfield

How might you unscramble the lithium hydroxide treatment if it is not working and can the process be reversed? I ask this because someone sent me an object that had been treated by the lithium hydroxide process and the surface is deteriorating and the object is falling to pieces. I do not know whether it is as a result of the treatment or not.

D. Watkinson

There will be lithium ion residues in the object, hydroxides, carbonates and chlorides will still be present because as I mentioned these are not all removed. If a low percentage of chloride is removed, say 35%, then the problem arises that the lithium chloride formed is, like ferric chloride, hygroscopic. At approximately 13 to 15% R.H. lithium hydroxide will absorb moisture and go into solution and hence aid corrosion of metallic iron. I cannot really see that it is the lithium hydroxide treatment that is causing the object to break up unless the formation of rust products during treatment has blocked the pores and is thus effectively sealing in the chlorides. It does not really seem you are in a worse position than you were to start with, you have removed some of the chlorides and that must be beneficial to some extent but you have not removed enough to stabilize the object. You can try soaking the object in ethanol which will remove lithium chloride if it is there.

C. Haywood

Is there any advantage in using lithium hydroxide in combination with boiling instead of boiling alone for those objects that can stand it and how does the lithium hydroxide method compare for time?

D. Watkinson

If you treat the object with lithium hydroxide solution followed by boiling, it does not appear to extract any more chloride than boiling alone. Also boiling alone is time consuming. When using lithium hydroxide only you can place the object in the solution and return to it at intervals.

APPLICATION OF THE ALKALINE SULPHITE TREATMENT TO ARCHAEOLOGICAL IRON: A COMPARATIVE STUDY OF DIFFERENT DESALINATION METHODS

A. Rinuy and F. Schweizer

Introduction

At the time of its creation a few years ago, the Research and Conservation Laboratory of the Musée d'art et d'histoire in Geneva was faced with the problem of conserving iron objects recovered from excavation sites. Without adequate treatment a badly corroded iron object risks total destruction if removed from the environment in which it has sojourned. In the earth, the iron is in contact with a certain amount of humidity, oxygen and chlorides which cause corrosion but once the object is excavated the increase in the oxygen concentration amplifies the phenomenon of corrosion. North and Pearson (1978), have described this problem very well, particularly in relation to archaeological objects recovered from the sea. Three constituents are mainly responsible for the corrosion of iron: water, oxygen and chlorides. From the theoretical point of view it may seem easier to eliminate water and oxygen from the object. In practice however, it would be unrealistic to hope to preserve museum objects on public display, in an atmosphere free from oxygen or moisture. The elimination of the chloride therefore appears the only possible solution. With certain exceptions (Oddy and Hughes, 1970; North and Pearson, 1975, 1978) results have not been forthcoming concerning the amount of chloride extracted from the corrosion layers of treated objects or the significance of residual chloride in the object. It was decided therefore, to study the comparative efficiency of the various desalination methods and the stabilization of corrosion. Six techniques are currently in use:–

1. Intensive washing in deionized water (Plenderleith and Werner, 1971).
2. Electrolytic desalination with cathodic connection (Wihr, 1972, 1975).
3. Electrolytic desalination with the object placed in an electric field (electrophoresis) (Eichhorn, 1975).
4. Desalination with sodium sesquicarbonate (Oddy and Hughes, 1970).
5. Reduction of iron chlorides and oxides with a hydrogen current at 400°C (North and Pearson, 1978) and at 800°C (Barkman, 1975).
6. Lithium hydroxide method (Bresle, 1974).

The fact that so many methods are in use clearly indicates that none is really satisfactory, either because they are insufficient or because they present the dangers of exfoliation or modification of the metallographic structure of the iron.

North and Pearson (1975), proposed a new method of desalination for marine iron objects which appears to present obvious advantages when compared to the other techniques:–

a. All the iron chlorides are dissolved, including the water insoluble ones.
b. The corrosion layers of the object are consolidated and stabilized.
c. The metallographic properties of the iron are not affected.
d. The method is simple and inexpensive and presents no apparent long term danger for the object.

The technique consists of dissolving the iron chlorides in an alkaline sulphite solution ($NaOH/Na_2SO_3$, 0.5M at 50°C). It is based on the fact that iron is stable in a strongly alkaline medium, even when chlorides are present. It was decided therefore to verify to what extent this method could be applied in the treatment of land-derived archaeological iron artifacts, and to study its effectiveness.

The investigation was divided into two parts. First, a comparison of different desalination techniques applied directly to excavated objects and a determination of the amount of chloride eliminated. Second, a study at successive stages of the distribution of chlorides in a corroded object and a quantitative determination of the distribution of chlorides in the corrosion layers and in the metal core respectively. Also a progressive destruction of the samples in order to determine the total quantity of chloride present in an object and the amount remaining after desalination.

To this end, the Württembergisches Landesmuseum, Stuttgart kindly placed at the disposal of the Research and Conservation Laboratory, several kilos of excavated Roman nails. These objects offered two important advantages; the possibility of working with relatively homogeneous material and the fact that permission was given to enable the nails to be destroyed after treatment so that the total amount of chloride present in the object could be determined. The amount of chloride eliminated during the desalination process was monitored electrochemically (Rinuy, 1979).

Comparison of the efficiency of five desalination methods by quantitative determination of the chlorides released

The fact that the Württembergisches Landesmuseum uses the electrophoresis method of desalination (Eichhorn, 1975) allowed a point of comparison with the alkaline sulphite method to be established as well as for the intensive washing technique (Plenderleith and Werner, 1971); immersion in a solution of 10% formic acid followed by the intensive washing technique; washing in distilled water at 40°C with daily changes of water (Wihr, 1975).

Separate samples (1kg) of nails were subjected to a number of treatments:–

a. Placed in 10% formic acid to eliminate traces of

The results of these treatments are shown in Table 15.

The results in Table 15 show that the alkaline sulphite desalination technique releases twice the amount of chloride when compared with other methods. It is also evident that the application of an electric current (Table 15.a) or heat (Table 15. c,d,e,) to the deionized water did not improve the water washing techniques. When objects were left in 10% formic acid for a few days, the same result was obtained.

It was concluded that half of the chloride in a corroded iron object consists of iron oxychlorides; insoluble in water but soluble in an alkaline medium. Since chlorides are active only when dissolved, these oxychlorides are harmless as long as they remain insoluble. Unfortunately, under the effects of

	mg of Cl⁻ eliminated per kg of nails by different desalination methods						Total
a. Electro-phoresis	:	n.d.*,	followed by	alkaline sulphite	:	240 mg	**
b. 10% Formic acid	:	223 mg	followed by	alkaline sulphite	:	212 mg	435 mg
c. Intensive washing	:	210 mg					210 mg
d. 10% Formic acid	:	220 mg	followed by	intensive washing	:	0 mg	220 mg
e. Distilled water at 40°C changed daily	:	240 mg					240 mg

n.d.* = not determined
** = the total amount of eliminated chloride could not be determined since the amount eliminated by electrophoresis had not been assessed in Stuttgart.

Table 15. Comparison of the efficiency of five desalination methods.

calcareous concretions and then washed in deionized water and placed in an electric field (electrophoresis). The nails were placed finally in an alkaline sulphite solution to determine whether any further chloride could be removed by this method.
b. Treated with 10% formic acid and then transferred directly to an alkaline sulphite solution.
c. Placed in deionized water and heated and cooled alternately (intensive washing).
d. Treated with 10% formic acid and subsequently by the intensive washing technique (as under c. above).
e. Washed in distilled water at 40°C; water changed daily.

humidity and time, they are converted into water soluble chlorides – especially if the water soluble chlorides have already been eliminated – and are ready once again to attack the iron core. It is therefore necessary to eliminate the water insoluble chlorides if further corrosion is to be prevented. After treatment with deionized water however, the residual chloride in the object is equal to the amount removed; thus the efficiency of alkaline sulphite treatment is proved. Objects can remain in the alkaline sulphite solution for months, even years, before being restored. The corrosion layers are in fact consolidated by the treatment. Artifacts decorated with silver and brass which were subjected to the treatment suffered no damage.

Distribution of chloride in a corroded iron object and a determination of the amount of chloride eliminated by the alkaline sulphite treatment.

The initial investigations detailed above have shown that the alkaline sulphite treatment removes twice as much chloride than do other desalination methods. The second part of this investigation concerns:–
a. The determination of the total amount of chloride in a corroded object.
b. The distribution of water soluble and water insoluble chlorides in the corroded regions and the metal core respectively (in general the nails used still contained a metal core).
c. The residual chloride level in the object after desalination.

To obtain this information an attempt was made to dissolve the nails but this was hindered by the excessive amounts of rust. It was decided finally to file down the nails thus obtaining a finely divided powder. Samples of untreated nails obtained in this manner were placed first in 10% formic acid and then into alkaline sulphite solution to determine the total amount of chloride present and the ratio of water soluble to water insoluble chlorides.

The total amount of chloride present in the nails varied from one batch to another as some nails were much more corroded than others. The ratio of water soluble to water insoluble chlorides however, remained constant:–

$$H_2O \text{ soluble } Cl^- \quad : \quad H_2O \text{ insoluble } Cl^-$$
$$3 \quad : \quad 1$$

After treatment with deionized water, half the chlorides remained in the object whereas it was expected that only a quarter should remain. It was thought that deionized water fails to penetrate sufficiently into the corrosion layers and does not succeed in eliminating all the water soluble chlorides present in the object.

In further batches of nails the distinction was made between the corroded outer layers and the metal core; these were desalinated separately first in 10% formic acid and then in alkaline sulphite solution. The same ratio of water soluble to water insoluble chlorides was observed both in the corroded regions and on the surface of the metal core; the ratio of 3:1 remained constant.

When the corrosion layers were removed before desalination it was observed that the amount of chloride on the surface of the metal core was almost equal to that in the corrosion products (80%). Such a large concentration of chloride at the active corrosion site would lead to a gradual but inevitable destruction of the metal core.

To verify the efficiency and effectiveness of the alkaline sulphite reduction treatment further investigations were made in order:–

a. To determine the depth of penetration of the desalination treatment into the corroded regions.
b. To determine the residual chloride in the object after desalination and the proportion it represents in comparison with the total amount of chloride eliminated at each stage.
c. To determine whether after the alkaline sulphite treatment the object could be considered as being stabilized, or whether there was a danger of further corrosion due to the residual chloride in the object.

Untreated nails were desalinated first in 10% formic acid and then in alkaline sulphite solution. The corrosion layers were removed and the desalination treatment described above was then applied separately to the corrosion layers and the metal cores. Finally, the metal cores were filed down and desalinated for a third time in order to determine the total amount of chloride contained in the nails before desalination and the residual chloride after desalination.

Results and discussion

From 1kg of corroded nails, 223mg of chloride was extracted by immersion in 10% formic acid and a further 212mg by the alkaline sulphite treatment (Table 16.a). By removing the corrosion layers from this kilogram of nails, 406g of corrosion products and 594g of metallic core was obtained. These two fractions were treated separately as described above. No further chloride was extracted by the formic acid but a small amount was removed by the alkaline sulphite solution, being 11mg and 7mg respectively for the corrosion products and the metal core (Table 16.b). Nearly all the chlorides were extracted during the course of the first treatment applied to the nails (Table 16.a).

In contrast to deionized water, alkaline sulphite penetrates through the corrosion layers down to the metal core. Alkaline sulphite is a wetting agent, its interfacial surface tension measured experimentally is two times lower than that of deionized water. The alkaline sulphite treatment therefore removes the chlorides from the areas where they are most concentrated, active and damaging: on the surface of the metal core.

After the second desalination the metal cores were filed down and desalinated for a third time; 13mg of chloride were extracted by the 10% formic acid and 93mg by the alkaline sulphite solution (Table 16.c). This 106mg chloride represents the residual chloride in 1kg of nails after desalination by the alkaline sulphite treatment.

By summing the quantities of chloride extracted

		mg of chloride extracted by different desalination methods				
treatment	weight of nails	10% formic acid	followed by	alkaline sulphite	total eliminated	residual chloride
a. desalination	1 kg	223 mg				336 mg
			+	212 mg	435 mg	124 mg
b. removal of corrosion layers followed by desalination	406 g corrosion + 594 g metal cores	0 mg + 0 mg	+ +	11 mg 7 mg	18 mg	106 mg
c. filing of the metal cores and desalination	594 g of fillings	13 mg	+	93 mg	106 mg	<0.1 mg
				total	559 mg	

Table 16. Efficiency of the alkaline sulphite treatment: small residual chloride levels after desalination.

at all the stages described above a total of 559mg chloride is obtained. Desalination in 10% formic acid or distilled water (electrophoresis, intensive washing, washing in distilled water at 40°C with daily changes of water) removed only 223mg of chloride and left 336mg of chloride in the nails (Table 15. c,d,e, and Table 16.a). Further treatment in the alkaline sulphite solution removed another 212mg of chloride and left therefore only 124mg in the nails; that is three times less (Table 16.a).

If the corrosion layers are removed down to the metal core prior to desalination, another 3% of chloride can be extracted (Table 16.b). After desalination with the alkaline sulphite solution 106mg of chloride remained in the 1kg of corroded nails (Table 16.b). These chlorides are located essentially in the metallic core of the nails. Their concentration is therefore only of importance for the 594g of remaining metal. To determine whether this quantity of chloride presents a danger of subsequent corrosion, i.e. whether the residual chloride concentration is high enough to reactivate corrosion, was investigated. The purpose of these experiments was to define the minimum chloride concentration level required to initiate active corrosion in iron in the presence of air and humidity.

Determination of the 'critical chloride level' for corrosion

The experiments were carried out with small polished iron plates. They were covered with solutions containing increasing amounts of chloride and placed in a wet chamber. The experimental conditions were not identical to those of archaeological iron objects, since the samples were subjected to an homogeneous solution of chlorides whereas chlorides are distributed unevenly in excavated objects. The conditions under which the iron plates were tested were therefore extreme as the high levels of humidity and oxygen were conducive to active corrosion of the iron.

Six polished iron plates were coated with synthetic resin (araldite) except for an area in the centre of each plate measuring 2cm × 1.5cm (3cm^2). The exposed surfaces were then exposed with chloride solutions in quantities of 0.6ml per plate (Table 17). The plates were placed in a wet chamber (95% relative humidity) at room temperature.

Results

Test plates 1 and 2 were rapidly covered with a thin layer of rust, but there was no further corrosion. The iron appeared to be stablized. After four years there was no apparent change.

Test plates 3 and 4 revealed slightly more corrosion but also became stabilized. The difference in corrosion between plates 3 and 4 was minimal. A chloride concentration of 10^{-3}M or 10^{-2}M is apparently not very dangerous. But a higher level of chloride concentration results in active corrosion. Test plates 5 and 6, subjected to amounts of 2.1mg $Cl^-0.6ml^{-1}$ and 21mg $Cl^-0.6ml^{-1}$ respectively, were almost totally destroyed. At the end of four years,

Test plate No.	Solution	Chloride content
1	deionoized water	0mg Cl^-
2	tap water	0.007mg Cl^- ml^{-1}(0.0042mg Cl^-0.6ml^{-1})
3	KCl 10^{-3}M	0.035mg Cl^{-1}(0.021mg Cl^-0.6ml^{-1})
4	KCl 10^{-2}M	0.35mg Cl^{-1} (0.21mg Cl^-0.6ml^{-1})
5	KCl 10^{-1}M	3.5mg Cl^- ml^{-1} (2.1mg Cl^-0.6ml^{-1})
6	KCl 1.0M	35.0mg Cl^- ml^{-1} (21.0mg Cl^-0.6ml^{-1})

Table 17. Concentration of chloride solutions for the determination of the 'critical chloride level' for corrosion.

test plate 6 was almost entirely corroded. Corrosion is induced by a minimum of 0.021mg Cl^- 0.6ml^{-1} and becomes acute when the level of chloride concentration is above 2.1mg Cl^-0.6ml^{-1}.

Returning to the question of the residual chloride in the nails after desalination with the alkaline sulphite treatment, i.e. 106mg of chloride per 594g of metal filings. This 594g comes from the remaining metal core of approximately 145 nails. An estimate of the surface area of the remaining metal cores gives a value of approximately 1240cm^2 (surface measured for 10 nails: 85.5cm^2). If it is assumed that after desalination the 106mg of chloride are uniformly distributed on the surface of the metal cores, a value of 0.08mg Cl^-1cm^{-2}, that is 0.24mg Cl^- 3cm^{-2}, is obtained.

Comparing this result with those for the test plates, the chloride concentration corresponds to test plate 4, that is slight initial corrosion followed by stabilization. In estimating the exposed area however, only the measurable surface of the metal cores was taken into account whereas in reality the chlorides are distributed in the corroded object through cracks and breaks. Thus, the above value is probably an underestimate of the actual surface exposed to chlorides. The effective chloride concentration level was therefore lower, if not below, the 'critical chloride level'. The 'critical chloride level' may in fact also vary according to the micro-climate around the object and the type of iron.

The 106mg of residual chloride expressed in parts per million (ppm) of the weight of the treated objects (1kg of nails) corresponds to 106ppm. As the 106mg of chloride are only of importance to the 594g of remaining metallic core it in fact represent 170ppm. North and Pearson (1978), estimated a residual chloride level of 200ppm as safe for the treated object whereas 1000ppm or more was thought to lead to the destruction of the iron object. The nails treated here may therefore be considered to be stabilized. Long-term exposure for four months in a wet chamber at 95% relative humidity has so far revealed no evidence of rust. Objects such as Roman chisels and belt buckles were also left for four months in a wet chamber after being treated with alkaline sulphite. No rust formation has so far been observed. It may be assumed therefore, that corrosion in these artifacts has now been stabilized.

Conclusions

The alkaline sulphite treatment for desalination has now been adopted as a standard procedure in the Research and Conservation Laboratory at the Musée d'art et d'histoire, Geneva for the treatment of badly corroded land-derived iron objects. In view of the results obtained in the course of this research it has been concluded that the alkaline sulphite treatment is the only desalination technique which it is believed in no way endangers the object but on the contrary consolidates it. At the same time the chloride content is reduced to a level at which corrosion is stabilized. The process is long but treatment can start immediately after excavation and the artifacts can remain in the alkaline sulphite solution for several months or even longer while awaiting restoration, without suffering damage. A cannon left in alkaline sulphite solution for two and a half years has suffered no observable damage.

The quantitative research undertaken and the results obtained confirmed the efficiency of the alkaline sulphite treatment. It is the opinion of the authors that this treatment combines all the advantages of desalination and has no damaging effects.

Acknowledgements

We wish to thank Mr. Durand and Mr. Houriet, restorers at the Research and Conservation Laboratory, Musée d'art et d'histoire, Geneva, for their technical assistance and, in particular, for filing down the Roman nails used in this research project.

Our thanks also go to Mr. Eichhorn and the Director of the Landesmuseum, Stuttgart for kindly providing us with the excavated Roman nails, and for participating in the comparative study of desalination techniques.

Dr. Pearson and Dr. North's research on the alkaline sulphite reduction treatment of marine iron incited us to undertake this study. We thank Dr. North for his interest and advice.

We are grateful to Dr. C. Lapaire, Director, Musée d'art et d'histoire, Geneva for his encouragement.

References

Barkman, L., Corrosion and conservation of iron. *Conservation in Archaeology and the Applied Arts. Stockholm Congress,* 1975, pp.169-172.

Bresle, A., Nya metoder för konservering av antikvariska järnföremål. *Jernkont. Ann. 158* 1974, pp.33-36.

Eichhorn, P., Eisenkonservierung und Restaurierung am Württembergischen Landesmuseum. *Arbeitsblätter. 8 Gr.1* 1975, pp.74-80.

North, N.A. and Pearson, C., Alkaline sulphite reduction treatment of marine iron. *ICOM Committee for Conservation, 4th Triennial Meeting, Venice,* 1975, pp.1-14. (75/13/3).

North, N.A., and Pearson, C., Methods for treating marine iron. *ICOM Committee for Conservation, 5th Triennial Meeting, Zagreb,* 1978, pp.1-10. (78/23/3).

Oddy, W.A. and Hughes, M.J., The stabilization of 'active' bronze and iron by the use of sodium sesquicarbonate. *Studies in Conservation. 15* 1970, pp.183-189.

Plenderleith, H.J. and Werner, A.E.A., *The Conservation of Antiquities and Works of Art.* 2nd Ed. 1971. Oxford University Press, London.

Rinuy, A., Vergleichende Untersuchungen zur Entsalzung von Eisenfunden. *Arbeitsblätter. 12 Gr.1* 1979, pp.130-140.

Wihr, R., Elektrolytische Metallentsalzung. *Arbeitsblätter. 2 Gr.1* 1972, pp.31-48.

Wirh, R. Electrolytic desalination of archaeological iron. *Conservation in Archaeology and the Applied Arts. Stockholm Congress,* 1975, pp.189-194.

WHY DO SOME IRON OBJECTS BREAK UP IN STORE?

B. Knight

Introduction

All conservators will be familiar with objects which have completely disintegrated in storage. There are basically two ways in which this happens; they either break into wedges (Fig.31) or flakes (Fig.32). Completely mineralised objects, or those with only a small iron core, tend to break into wedges. More solid objects either split off small dish-shaped flakes or large flat ones. Fig.31 shows what is commonly found; that once the object has disentegrated it cannot be re-assembled without leaving gaps. The pieces have actually shrunk irreversibly.

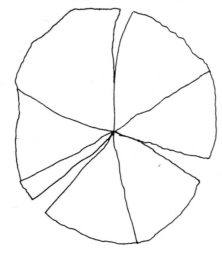

Fig. 31. Disintegration of a completely mineralised object into wedges

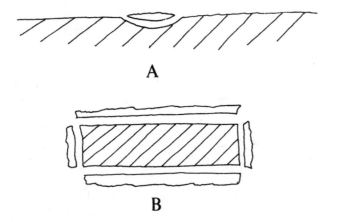

Fig. 32. 'Dishing' (A) and 'flaking' (B) of incompletely corroded iron objects

The chemical nature of the corrosion layers

The main components are magnetite (Fe_3O_4) and goethite (α-FeOOH) (Turgoose, this volume). Fig.33 shows schematically a cross-section of a typical corroded iron object. This is the likely structure of an object that has been lying undisturbed in fairly non-aggressive conditions for many years. In the

centre is the iron core, which of course disappears in a completely mineralised object. This is surrounded by the magnetite layer, which appears dark grey and

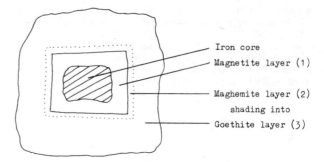

Fig. 33. Schematic cross-section of a corroded iron object

is magnetic. In most objects there is a fairly sharp boundary between this layer and the next, which is dark brown, magnetic and which can be seen under the microscope to contain soil minerals (sand grains etc). This boundary represents the original surface of the object, but it cannot necessarily be seen on all objects. The second layer fades off into the third, which is orange-brown, non-magnetic, softer and more porous than the second. The third layer consists largely of goethite intermixed with soil minerals, and the second layer is probably maghemite (γ-Fe$_2$O$_3$). This is poorly crystallised and difficult to identify by X-ray diffraction as the lines tend to be faint and there is considerable overlap with the lines for magnetite (JCPDS cards 15-615 and 19-629). It is likely that there is a gradual change in average oxidation number from the incompletely oxidised magnetite (ox.no. $2\frac{2}{3}$) to the completely oxidised goethite (ox.no. 3).

As mentioned above, magnetite and goethite are the stable corrosion products which are commonly found on iron objects. There are however two other ferric oxide hydroxides, akaganéite (β-FeOOH) and lepidocrocite (γ-FeOOH), both of which are less stable than goethite, and change slowly into goethite. In spite of its instability, akaganéite is important in the breaking up of objects after excavation. Referring to Figs.31 and 32, it will often be found that the inner surfaces of the flakes are covered with an orange powder; this is akaganéite. It seems that the crystals are actually forcing the flakes off, and that the disintegration is the combined result of this and the shrinkage.

To understand how akaganéite forms one must consider what happens in the course of corrosion of an iron object underground. Iron is dissolved at anodic regions and oxygen is reduced at cathodic regions, and the ions such as chloride and sulphate which are present in the soil water are attracted to the anodic regions and are concentrated there. As corrosion progresses, the corrosion front proceeds further into the interior of the object, so that the anions are drawn deep inside. This is why it is so difficult to wash the chloride out of iron objects.

Before the object is dug up and allowed to dry out the magnetite layer, which must be quite porous and which also contain small cracks, will be saturated with water. After excavation the magnetite starts to dry out and ferrous ions and chloride and sulphate ions will be drawn out towards the surface to a greater or lesser extent. As they do so they will meet atmospheric oxygen diffusing inwards. What happens next will depend on the relative humidity, the composition and concentration of the ionic solution, the amount of oxygen present and the rate of drying.

If the sulphate concentration is high and the drying is fairly rapid, ferrous sulphate may crystallise out in the form of a white powder (rozenite $FeSO_4.4H_4O$, JCPDS card 16-699), sometimes seen on fractured surfaces. It is fairly stable, not very hygroscopic and is oxidised by air only slowly. A possible end product is jarosite, typically $NaFe_3(OH)_6(SO_4)_2$ (JCPDS card 11-302), a basic ferric sulphate. This is sometimes found as lemon-yellow powdery patches on the outer surfaces of objects.

If the chloride concentration is high and conditions are fairly damp, objects may be found to be sweating, that is with globules of liquid appearing on the surface. Although the liquid looks brown, it does contain ferrous ion. It also contains a lot of chloride and is quite acidic. Because ferrous chloride is very hygroscopic crystals are not formed unless the object is intensively dried. Crystalline $FeCl_2.4H_2O$ has been identified on an iron object (Wyles and Biek, in press). Usually the ferrous ion is oxidised and hydrolysed, and eventually forms very characteristic thin spherical shells which are often found on the surface of objects.

Akaganéite also forms when a solution containing ferrous ions and chloride ions is allowed to oxidise (Mackay, 1962). If the oxidation is rapid because there is easy access for oxygen then crystallisation is rapid and very small crystals form. If this occurs in the cracks and pores in the corrosion layers the effect will be to push flakes off. If on the other hand the ferrous plus chloride solution is trapped inside the object it will oxidise only slowly. This happens for instance in the interior of a completely hollow object or inside a rust bubble. Akaganéite can then form quite large (1-2mm) crystals in the form of thin hexagonal plates. As these crystals form inside an existing void they do not tend to do any damage. The void itself is however a point of weakness, which is why objects may break at such a place.

As mentioned above, akaganéite is not stable in the long term. Within a few years it is converted into goethite and the colour changes from orange to brown. In the process, the chloride ions which are trapped in the akaganéite crystals are released and can stimulate further corrosion (Keller, 1969). Akaganéite is often found in actively corroding areas (Zucchi, Morigi and Bertolasi, 1977), and where it occurs in contact with metallic iron it can accelerate corrosion (Keller, 1969).

How to prevent objects from breaking up in store

Two reasons for objects breaking up in store have been suggested. The first is shrinkage of the magnetite layer due to dehydration. The second is flaking, caused partly by dehydration and partly by akaganéite forming inside the corrosion layers. The shrinkage can be avoided by preventing the object from drying out and the formation of akaganéite can be avoided likewise by preventing oxidation. The answer therefore appears to be that freshly excavated objects should be kept damp, and access of oxygen should be prevented.

On reflection, these suggestions should not seem too surprising if the environment of an object buried in the ground is considered. It is damp; the relative humidity of the air in the soil pores is close to 100%, access of oxygen is limited and the temperature is fairly low and uniform. All of these factors change on excavation; the object dries out, access of oxygen is much greater and the average temperature is higher and subject to fluctuation. Small wonder therefore if objects start to deteriorate rapidly after excavation!

Experiments are now taking place using a representative selection of objects from various sites which are being stored under different conditions:–

1. Control – no special packing
2. Dry storage – fresh silica gel in a sealed container
3. Damp storage – objects kept in soil in a sealed container
4. Damp storage with reduced oxygen – objects stored in a sealed container with pads soaked in alkaline sulphite solution to remove oxygen
5. Storage in cold alkaline sulphite solution in a sealed container (Rinuy and Schweizer, this volume).

The results will be presented in due course.

References

Keller, P., Vorkommen, Entstehung und Phasenumwandlung von β −FeOOH in Rost. *Werkstoffe und Korrosion. 20* 1969, pp.102-108.

Mackay, A.L., β −Ferric oxide hydroxide. *Mineralogical Magazine. 33* 1962, pp.270-280.

Zucchi, F. Morigi, G. and Bertolasi, V., Beta iron oxide hydroxide formation in localised active corrosion of iron artifacts. *Corrosion and Metal Artifacts. (ed. B.F. Brown et al)* 1977, pp.103-105. (NBS Special Publication 479, U.S. Government Printing Office, Washington D.C. 1977).

DISCUSSION
Chairman:
D. Leigh

V. Daniels
How do you determine chloride in the presence of sodium sulphite as my experience has been that this is very difficult?

A. Rinuy
You have to eliminate the sodium sulphite. When we take a sample of the solution we add concentrated nitric acid to make the solution very acidic, add deionized water and slowly evaporate the solution; the sulphite goes to the sulphate and evaporates. You are then able to determine the chloride content.

V. Daniels
Did you determine the level of chloride in the sodium sulphite you purchased? Some sources contain quite large amounts of chloride.

A. Rinuy
The sodium sulphite has to be very pure.

J. Ashley-Smith
Dr. Knight has said we should keep iron objects damp and Mr. Black suggested we should keep them dry and showed a picture of the use of silica gel as a desiccant. I just wanted to point out, silica gel is only a desiccant if it is dry. Silica gel is merely a hygroscopic or porous material and therefore even when it is blue, in the self indicating form, it can maintain a relative humidity of up to 50% above it. Only if it has been thoroughly dried and maintained dry will it be an efficient desiccant.

B. Knight
If you have the object in a plastic bag with a handful of silica gel, the polythene bag is by no means impermeable to water vapour, so that in a fairly short time the environment inside the bag will be similar to that outside. The important thing is to keep the air out as well because if you have the object in a plastic bag you are going to be worse off. You can never exclude the air totally but it is something to do at least in the interim between excavation and treatment. We want to cut that period down as much as possible because we know that periods of 6 months to several years are commonplace.

S. Blackshaw
Would it be worth somebody investigating storage under inert gases or at reduced pressures?

B. Knight
Yes, but this is expensive and cannot be used on site.

S. Blackshaw
I cannot see how a box of soil is actually excluding air and that these plastic boxes are air tight?

B. Knight
The plastic boxes are fairly air tight and the seal is extremely efficient.

K. Foley
Is it true to say that if you do manage to keep your objects really dry, cured in silica gel in a plastic box it will be safe? It seems to me that there is far more control over the atmosphere if you can monitor the relative humidity you have got in a box. You know that you have oxygen there as an undetermined variable but you can measure the relative humidity to see if it really is low. It was said earlier that a relative humidity of approximately 5% was not safe.

B. Knight
You are safe from further corrosion. The point is you are not safe from the dehydration that causes the shrinkage and hence causes the object to flake and fall apart.

D. Barker
In home brewing you can use camden tablets to keep the air and also the oxygen out. In the alkaline sulphite method you may be doing just that, by keeping the air or the oxygen out of the system there will be no corrosion.

A. Rinuy
I think it is very difficult to keep oxygen and water out and the least difficult think to do is to remove the chloride. You always have oxygen and water in a museum.

D. Barker
In the electricity industry, in small power stations, they remove oxygen from the feed water by adding chemicals such as hydrazine or sodium metabisulphite. These chemicals are added purely to remove the oxygen and they get the levels down do below 1ppm. Could you not store you objects in such solutions?

A. Rinuy
You can store objects in alkaline sulphite.

D. Barker
Storing in this solution may then be removing the oxygen and not necessarily removing all the chlorides?

B. Knight
As it is an alkaline solution it is acting as an inhibitor and is also absorbing oxygen and soaking out chlorides.

D. Barker
You thought sulphate was not really important or you passed over it. If you look at the corrosion rates in industrial atmospheres they are quite a lot higher than they are in the marine environment. I think

ferrous sulphate is just as important except that in many of the specimens we have looked at they do not necessarily have a high ferrous sulphate content. Would sulphates be important if you had an object from an industrial site or sulphates produced from underground bacterial corrosion?

B. Knight
What happens underground is very different from what happens in the atmosphere or under the sea and I am mostly concerned with land based archaeology. I am not saying that sulphates are harmless but they are less of a problem on the whole than the chlorides. It is the formation of akaganéite which causes a lot of this flaking whereas the sulphates do not do that.

J. Cronyn
Dr. Knight was saying that it was the shrinkage of the magnetite as it dries which was one of the problems and you are saying that with the alkaline sulphite you are producing magnetite. Do you have any problems with objects shrinking when you take them out?

F. Schweizer
The magnetite we are producing from what we think is the conversion of the oxychlorides is a very small amount of the total corrosion products. We checked this very carefully and you do not change the goethite or the $\gamma-FeOOH$ in the alkaline sulphite solution. There is no evidence so far to suggest any reduction of new corrosion layers to magnetite. I think there is some confusion about preserving objects from excavation into the laboratory up to the time it is going to be treated and conserving it after treatment for the future. I don't think quite honestly that you can keep oxygen out for ever but we must do what we can to make sure that the objects survive as long as possible. It's all very well to keep oxygen out up to the point when you conserve the object but it does not replace the conservation treatment. I think there is no doubt, that as long as you have a metal core left it will be attacked by chlorides and moisture. We should do what we can to make the objects completely stable even if it means training the archaeologists to be patient and wait until the treatment is finished. It is pointless to excavate and then to have the object just fade away.

M. Corfield
When we get our objects from excavation we tend to store them until such time as we are able to carry out our physical and chemical cleaning processes and having done that we stabilize the objects. From what you are saying you carry out the stabilization process before you clean which seems a more logical way of doing things.

A. Rinuy
Yes, I think so. You get corrosion from three things – chlorides, oxygen and water. If you remove the chlorides you can stabilize the object. So if when you excavate your objects you start to eliminate the chlorides you are both stabilizing the object and preventing further corrosion.

M. Corfield
Do you have to re-stabilize the object after cleaning?

A. Rinuy
Not with respect to chlorides but perhaps for consolidation.

B. Knight
I think we are in agreement that the important thing is to preserve the object after excavation and until we can get time to look at it. Then we can make a decision on which objects we want to preserve. We must keep them all until we can make that decision without the objects deciding for us by falling apart.

S. Turgoose
I think I'm right in saying that you decided that the chlorides that were soluble in 10% formic acid were the water soluble chlorides and then the alkaline sulphite took out more besides that. Did you try using 0.5M NaOH instead of 10% formic acid to test for water soluble chlorides because the pH of these two solutions is very different; one is about pH13 and the other pH2 to pH3?

A. Rinuy
We started with formic acid because we wanted to remove the concretions as well, that was our intention, it was not to remove chlorides. We then checked the chloride levels and found that there was a lot of chloride coming out so we put the objects first into formic acid and then into alkaline sulphite.

S. Turgoose
If you have got adsorption of the chlorides onto the geothite, I think this is a very pH dependent phenomenon?

F. Schweizer
In our experiments we first removed the corrosion layers and treated the metal core and the corrosion layers separately. You even get insoluble chlorides in the metal core so it cannot be chlorides associated with the goethite, because there is no goethite there. Also we cannot prove it by X-ray diffraction. We still think there must be insoluble chlorides around and the only compound we can think of is the ferrous FeOCl.

S. Turgoose
It's hardly insoluble, it's not really stable in moist air.

A. Rinuy

If you file down the metal core without any corrosion layers and put it first into formic acid or water you remove some of the chlorides. If then you place it in alkaline sulphite you remove a further amount of the chloride. There is no adsorption effect.

S. Turgoose

The chlorides in the metal core; they are not actually within the metal core they are the corrosion products which have penetrated some way down between the grains or into the spaces between the metal, not actually within the metal?

F. Schweizer

If you take a nail and cool it down with liquid nitrogen and break it you find the chloride is sitting in the metal core, because you get cracks. It's not within the metal structure I agree, it's what you might call physically within the metal core.

S. Turgoose

I was wondering about FeOCl because it seems there is no evidence for its presence and there is not enough of the deposit there for us to identify it positively. I could account for the presence of insoluble chlorides in a number of other ways.

K. Kendell

You mentioned that threequarters of the chloride content was water soluble and one quarter wasn't. Also that the alkaline sulphite did not remove all that threequarters but only half. You then went on to say that if you get greater than 200ppm chloride in your iron then it was not stable, if it was less than 200ppm then it was stable. That would put a limit on the maximum amount of chloride you could have in your artifact before treatment to guarantee that the alkaline sulphite treatment is going to work. Because if a quarter of all your insoluble chlorides is greater than 200ppm then your artifact will not be stable?

A. Rinuy

When you wash with water your remove half of all the chlorides, but when you file down the sample we find we have in fact removed three quarters of them. We think that the alkaline sulphite penetrates better through the corrosion layers to the metal core.

K. Kendell

But if your alkaline sulphite does not remove the water insoluble chlorides and you have 15% of the chlorides remaining, if that 15% is greater than 200ppm then you have not got a stable object?

A. Rinuy

The alkaline sulphite does remove the insoluble chlorides. What we think to be water insoluble chlorides – insoluble FeOCl – this is soluble in alkaline sulphite.

F. Schweizer

It is a matter of diffusion of the chlorides. If all the chloride was accessible to the sodium sulphite solution it would all be dissolved.

K. Kendell

Is that to say that any chloride that is not accessible to the alkaline sulphite treatment is not going to cause further corrosion, or is not available for further corrosion, and that your process is only 85% efficient in the removal of chlorides?

A. Rinuy

You need a certain chloride concentration to initiate corrosion. With our experiments we found that if you have less than 200ppm then there is no corrosion. If the penetration of the alkaline sulphite is good enough to leave only 200ppm then this is not dangerous to the object.

K. Kendell

If the 15% of chloride remaining is greater than 200ppm then the alkaline sulphite treatment has not rendered that artifact stable and therefore there must be a maximum limit on the amount of chloride to start with?

F. Schweizer

Based on the nail samples in our experiments 200ppm represented, by accident, 15% chloride. What is difficult is to remove the very small amount remaining.

A. Rinuy

What is dangerous is that the chlorides remaining in the metal core may be active. You cannot penetrate the metal core with water to remove the chlorides.

K. Kendell

You think that the alkaline sulphite treatment would always get you down to 200ppm or less?

A. Rinuy

From what we have found in our experiments, yes.

K. Foley

What you seem to be suggesting is a possible method of storing iron safely by starting with the excavated material and putting it possibly into alkaline sulphite solution until such time that the treatment is finished and you can then take the object out and clean it. What happens to things that are contained in the corrosion layers such as tin, brass, silver, cloth impressions etc, and is the sort of thing you are doing going to render these very important archaeological details indistinguishable?

A. Rinuy

It is not dangerous. The example of the belt buckle we treated contained silver and brass and that was maintained for over 5 months in alkaline sulphite without being affected. On another belt we found that there was still a piece of textile attached as well as some silver.

K. Foley

It has no stripping effect?

F. Schweizer

No, not at all, we checked this very carefully. We prepared samples of the corrosion products and treated them separately and it does not change or dissolve them. I do not at present advise putting a lot of wood in alkaline sulphite solution but we are currently investigating its effect on wood. After two months, results are promising but it is too early yet to recommend its use for large quantities of wood.

ORGANIC COATINGS FOR IRON: A REVIEW OF METHODS

M. W. Pascoe

Iron objects when cleaned must be protected, for rarely can the atmosphere be assuredly maintained at a low humidity. Even in dry air, residual amounts of water will be trapped in fine pores, for the vapour pressure is lowered at a concave meniscus. The effect is exaggerated by any soluble salts whose concentration and chemical activity would be enhanced by evaporation of water from a pore. Whilst these fundamental considerations suggest that infinite conservation is unattainable, the exclusion of air, acid gases and oxygen from iron certainly proves beneficial. The barrier properties are important, and they are difficult to achieve. Many primers contain corrosion inhibitors though some make the films opaque. The practical requirements demand a resistance to handling and some ductility to cope with thermal expansion and volume changes from mild corrosion. Coatings should be intact and uniform and should be both repairable and removable.

Such a severe specification is difficult to meet, but by reviewing various methods of application some alternative strategies may be conceived. Solids can be melted and applied in various ways. Impregnation by immersion in melts, such as waxes, assisted by a vacuum, is a useful technique. Waxes can however become oxidised during melting and whilst this may improve the wetting of the iron surface through the development of carboxyl groups, there will also be some thermal degradation. A good barrier property demands a crystalline film, but the crystalline waxes may not be sufficiently ductile to accommodate strain from thermal and mechanical shock. Waxes plasticised with oils would be mechanically more suitable, but would be expected to have less crystallinity and hence less durability as the plasticiser slowly evaporates. The most cogent arguments against wax are its mechanical properties and the difficulty in controlling its thickness.

Poly(ethylene) is essentially a high molecular weight edition of paraffin wax, but its melts are too viscous for common use. However, like other thermoplastic polymers, poly(amides)-nylons poly(propylene), they can be applied as coatings by immersion of a hot iron object into a cold fluidised bed of air-agitated polymer particles. This powder coating technique is however not suitable for musueum objects for the films are liable to be porous and uneven because the thickness of the object is uneven. Plastisols may appear to be satisfactory: these are a dispersion, usually of poly (vinyl chloride), in plasticisers which, when heated afterwards to 180°C, homogenise and form a gel. This is used to coat wire frames, cotton gloves, steel sheeting, etc. However, when any externally plasticised compound is considered, the fact that evaporative plasticiser loss causes hardening and must leave voids for the subsequent access of air and water

makes it a poor candidate. As the thickness is considerable and as heating causes the poly(vinyl chloride) to release hydrogen chloride gas, which adds to the problems of corrosion, the use of plastisols is unlikely to find favour.

For many years conservators have been using solutions of polymers for coating objects: shellac, soluble nylon, cellulose nitrate (plasticised), poly-(vinyl acetate), poly(butylmethacrylate), etc. The solution of any high molecular weight polymer always has a high viscosity even when dilute. Consequently there are both practical and theoretical difficulties in applying a perfect and uniform coating. Practical problems might include the use of contaminated brushes or damp compressed air for spraying, but the theoretical problems are less tractable. A solvent deposited coating must, in drying, loose solvent, perhaps up to 90% of its volume. Some solvent will be retained for a very long time because solvent molecules are attracted to the solute which, however, cannot readily condense to form a compact or even crystalline polymer film. Consequently the barrier properties can never be good; the film will be imperfectly formed with both voids and residual solvent which might facilitate the passage of gases and vapours. The operator always finds difficulty in applying a complete and even coat, though it is seldom that any tests of thickness and film integrity are made. Additional coats cause solvents to be readsorbed into the first coat which may also be disturbed by the very high shearing from brushing. The balance between components of different potency in a realistic mixture of solvents is thus disturbed, as it is when differential evaporation of the various solvents takes place from spray droplets, particularly from the smaller species. Changes in the solvent balances will affect the structural configuration of the film and therefore its barrier properties. Much more serious is the fundamental phenomenon of the withdrawal of a liquid film from sharp points and edges under the influence of forces from surface energy (surface tension). Thus the very points liable to become exposed through handling will have the thinnest coating and therefore be most liable to be centres of corrosion. This factor operates for all systems deposited at a liquid phase, and is more serious with thin films.

However there are processes using aqueous dispersions of polymer, which can be very high in solids (up to 55% w/w) and yet have extremely low viscosities, and which can deposit a film onto a metal surface under the influence of an electrical field. The dispersed particles on reaching the metal electrode are designed to form an instant gel which does not creep away from sharp points.

Though outwardly similar to electroplating, this type of electrodeposition is in fact self levelling and has a considerable throwing power. As the film is an electrical insulator, further deposition is restricted and redirected to a more remote uncoated area. Most of the applications for this priming system deposit polymer on the anode. The film has then to be cured, i.e. chemically cross linked, by heating, and the electrode process often causes some migration of metal ions (Fe^{+++}) into the film thus creating discolouration. However, clear colourless films can be prepared with cathodic systems, and although they also require curing in an oven, it is probable that radiation curing in one form or another might eventually allow us to coat objects perfectly and cure the films without heating. This type of deposition does not in itself require a curable polymer system. An early process for depositing wax from an emulsion is known, though even that would require heat to fuse the wax particles together.

Solvent free systems using liquids are available though they still bear the disadvantage of withdrawal from edges and sharp features. But there must be a mechanism for chemical curing, such as the oxidation of drying oils, such as linseed, soya or tung. These are unsaturated triglycerides which form a complex non-crystalline polymeric network as they become oxidised by the air. The autoxidation takes place slowly over a long period of time, leading to a brittle film whose internal stresses cause peeling. Such autoxidative systems release organic acids and aldehydes into the air as they cure. These polluting gases not only smell, but could be corrosive to other objects in confined spaces. Whilst the properties can be modified by copolymerisation with alkyds, (types of polyester), urethanes or vinyls, this deficiency is common to them all and is compounded by other faults such as yellowing. However the use of linseed oil illustrates one very important point: it wets iron oxide surfaces extremely efficiently and has, as a result, proved to be an effective medium for primers for rusty iron and steel over many years. Other media can scarcely match this excellent wetting property which allows much more intimate contact over the rough iron oxide surfaces. Normally wetting is prevented by contamination and the uncovered spots or cisses are potentially active centres of future corrosion.

Another example of an all liquid system is the epoxy resin cured by mixing with a diamine or polyamide oligomer. These react together to form a film with a notable chemical resistance, though the wetting and adhesion demands a very clean surface, such as may be obtained by blast cleaning or by hydrogen reduction. In practice epoxy primers also contain solvents, though in principle they need not. They may also contain other polymeric materials in solution such as coal tar and bitumen.

An unusual means of applying solvent free coatings of polymer is by flame spraying. Particles are injected via an air stream into an oxygen/propane flame, directed onto the surface which quickly cools

it. Whilst this seems an extreme process, it works quite well on poly(ethylene), poly(amides), epoxy and polyester compositions. For though it always leads to thick coatings, it also leads to the concept of forming a polymer file by polymerisation directly onto a surface. This strange process is eminently practical and can be used to deposit excellent barrier films of clear transparent crystalline polymer onto any substrate with thicknesses from about 2μm upwards. All that is necessary is to expose the object to clouds of the monomer, (xylylene or its derivitives), whereupon the coating forms without any heating but inevitably at a reduced pressure. Unlike the electrophoretic system which would only coat the metals and not insulators such as ivory, jewels, wood, etc., the poly (p-xylylene) forms on all surfaces. This system has the best barrier properties and should have a long life. Like many others it is difficult to remove, not because it is cross linked, but because it is intrinsically insoluble, an attribute which is doutbless enhanced by its high degree of crystallinity. This emphasises a fundamental dilemma, that good barrier properties are associated with crystallinity, and the same morphology implies that removal by solvents will be difficult.

Our work on plasma at the British Museum has shown that it is possible to remove, by cold oxidation in an argon/oxygen gas discharge, any oxidisable organic coating, which is converted to carbon dioxide and water vapour and pumped away.

A reducing plasma of hydrogen has also been developed and as this might be expected to leave a clean fresh surface, it merits some coating process that follows immediately without breaking the vacuum.

A wide variety of organic molecules will deposit a polymer coating on a surface exposed to a plasma discharge and without heating. These films are very diverse and their corrosion resistance properties are not well known or understood, but some research on this is being stimulated for the benefit of conservation in the future.

Such coatings however could not be expected to penetrate into pores, which in the case of archaeological iron is perhaps the most significant factor. The varieties of objects demands the use of a variety of coating systems. There is no panacea.

Suggested further reading

Boxall, J. and von Fraunhofer, A., *Concise Paint Technology*. 1977. Elek Science, London.

Machu, W., *Handbook of Electropainting Technology*. 1978. Electrochemical Publications Ltd.

Solomon, D.H., *The Chemistry of Organic Film Formers*. 1967. Wiley.

Tatton, W.H. and Drew, E.W., *Industrial Paint Application*. Butterworths.

Turner, G.P.A., *Introduction to Paint Technology*. 1967. Chapman and Hall.

Yeates, R.L., *Electroplating*. 1970. Robert Dryer Ltd.

Paint Technology Manual Part IV. The Application of Surface Coatings. Oil and Colour Chemists Association. 1965. Chapman and Hall.

THE ROLE OF CORROSION INHIBITORS IN THE CONSERVATION OF IRON

R. Walker

Introduction

Iron and steel are thermodynamically unstable in the presence of moisture. Hence corrosion occurs when iron is immersed in fresh or sea water, buried underground or exposed to moist air. The rate of attack and the composition of the corrosion products depend upon the metal and the environment. One common form of corrosion product is hydrated ferric oxide $Fe_2O_3.H_2O$ or rust which is very similar to certain iron ores. Because the rate of corrosion can be quite high, the iron in many artifacts has been completely converted to weak ferrous compounds.

There are several forms of iron including wrought iron (a mixture of iron silicate slag fibres in a matrix of relatively pure iron (called ferrite)), cast iron (containing more than 2% carbon) and steel (less than 2% carbon). There are several forms of cast iron including grey (with flake graphite), nodular (with spherical carbon), white (with combined carbon) and malleable (white cast iron which has been heated or annealed to improve the properties.)

Several very early oriental iron structures still survive today. This is probably because the iron was made with charcoal (and not oil or coal as today) so it was relatively pure and did not contain much sulphur. It is this sulphur which is particularly detrimental as it considerably increases the rate of corrosion. One famous metallurgical wonder of the world is the iron pillar near Delhi in India. This pillar is about 7.2m high and 1300 years old and is in good condition. The reasons for its preservation have been discussed by Wrangler (1972) and include:–

1. it is covered by a protective layer of oxide (magnetite) 50 to $600\mu m$ thick.
2. the local climate is dry and unpolluted.
3. the iron has a low sulphur and a high phosphorus content.
4. it has a large mass and heat capacity so it tends to remain dry.

Medieval British wrought iron has lasted well and is probably more corrosion resistant than mild steel. This iron has probably survived because the atmosphere was unpolluted and there was little, if any, sulphur dioxide so that the protective oxides could form and withstand the atmospheric attack.

It may be concluded from the survival of the Dehli Pillar that in order to preseve iron it is necessary to modify the composition of the metal, produce a protective surface coating, modify the environment or keep the article dry.

General corrosion reactions

All metals except gold form an oxide film when exposed to air at room temperature. This layer of oxide is protective against corrosion but can be dissolved or broken down by acids. In practice the oxide may be quite thick as most articles are heated during manufacture so that more oxidation can occur.

Corrosion is an electrochemical process and involves:–

1. anodic areas where oxidation occurs and electrons are produced.
$$M \rightarrow M^{n+} + ne \underline{\hspace{2cm}} (16)$$
2. cathodic areas where reduction occurs and electrons are consumed.
$$2H^+ + 2e \rightarrow H_2 \underline{\hspace{2cm}} (17)$$
$$O_2 + 2H_2O + 4e \rightarrow 4(OH)^- \underline{\hspace{1cm}} (18)$$
$$2H_2O + 2e \rightarrow 2(OH)^- + H_2 \underline{\hspace{0.5cm}} (19)$$
3. a metallic circuit between the anodic areas and cathodic areas through which the electrons (or electrical current) can flow.
4. an electrolyte in which both anode and cathode are in contact.

These electrodes may be separate metals, different constituents in an alloy (such as copper rich and zinc rich phases in brass) or different areas on the same specimen. The anodic areas are more reactive and can be cracks in an oxide coating, grain boundaries or impurities. The cathodic areas can be unbroken oxide, more noble metallic impurities or compounds such as sulphides or phosphides.

The electrons produced at the anode flow through the metallic circuit to produce the electric current and they are consumed at the cathode. The rate of production of electrons must be exactly equal to the rate of consumption. The amount of metal dissolved (or corroded) can be calculated from the quantity of electricity and Faraday's Laws of Electrolysis. The intensity of corrosion at the anode surface is related to the local anodic current density.

The rate of production of electrons at the anode must be exactly equal to the rate of consumption at the cathode. Thus if the rate of the anodic or cathodic process is reduced the rate of corrosion is also reduced. It is also possible to slow the rate of corrosion by increasing the resistance in the metallic and/or electrolytic circuit and this may be achieved by coating the metal surface or using pure water instead of impure water or sea-water.

Corrosion of iron

Iron can be attacked in water by a direct chemical process.

$$3Fe + 4H_2O \rightarrow Fe_3O_4 + 4H_2 \underline{\qquad}(20)$$

This is, however, a very slow process and the electrochemical reactions are more important.

The anodic reaction during the corrosion of iron is:—

$$Fe \rightarrow Fe^{2+} + 2e \underline{\qquad}(21)$$

This is a rapid reaction in most media. The rate of corrosion is controlled by the cathodic reaction. There are several cathodic processes depending upon the degree of aeration in the water (i.e. the amount of dissolved oxygen).

In deaerated solutions, such as exist in waterlogged clays or in mud at the bottom of rivers, the cathodic reactions are:—

$$2H^+ + 2e \rightarrow H_2 \underline{\qquad}(22)$$
$$2H_2O + 2e \rightarrow 2(OH)^- + H_2 \underline{\qquad}(23)$$

The products can combine:—
$$Fe^{2+} + 2(OH)^- \rightarrow Fe(OH)_2$$

The ferrous hydroxide may initially stay in solution but as more is formed it can precipitate on the metal surface and slow the reactions by acting as a barrier to the diffusion of the reactants and/or products.

In aerated solutions, such as exist in flowing water and in moist soil, alternative cathodic processes can occur:—

$$O_2 + 2H_2O + 4e \rightarrow 4(OH)^- \underline{\qquad}(24)$$
$$O_2 + 2H^+ + 4e \rightarrow 2(OH)^- \underline{\qquad}(25)$$

These can be faster and the rate of corrosion of iron may increase by a factor of 100-fold.

The products can combine:—

$$Fe^{2+} + 2(OH)^- \rightarrow Fe(OH)_2 \underline{\qquad}(26)$$
White

with limited oxygen present:—
$$6Fe(OH)_2 + O_2 \rightarrow 4H_2O + 2Fe_3O_4.H_2O \underline{\qquad}(27)$$
Green hydrated magnetite.

$$Fe_3O_4.H_2O \rightarrow H_2O + Fe_3O_4 \underline{\qquad}(28)$$
Black magnetite

with more oxygen present:—
$$4Fe(OH)_2 + O_2 \rightarrow 2H_2O + 2Fe_2O_3.H_2O \underline{\qquad}(29)$$
Rust-red/brown.

Hence the colour of the corrosion product depends upon the supply of oxygen and this may supply useful information about the history of an artifact.

Sulphur dioxide

This is an acidic gas which is very soluble in water (1,300 times more soluble than oxygen) and acts as a powerful stimulator of atmospheric corrosion of iron and steel. It may be produced naturally in the atmosphere as well as being formed in the burning of oil and coal. The gas is dissolved in rain and the following reactions may occur:—

$$Fe + SO_2 + O_2 \rightarrow FeSO_4 \underline{\qquad}(30)$$
$$4FeSO_4 + O_2 + 6H_2O \rightarrow 2Fe_2O_3.H_2O + 4H_2SO_4 \underline{\qquad}(31)$$
$$4H_2SO_4 + 4Fe + 2O_2 \rightarrow 4FeSO_4 + 4H_2O \underline{\qquad}(32)$$

Hence the sulphuric acid is regenerated (Schikorr, 1963). It is particularly difficult to remove in recesses where corrosion can continue under moist conditions although the surface appears to be dry.

Thus during storage and exhibition it is necessary to ensure complete removal of moisture from metallic objects. Unfortunately, it has been shown that once the sulphates have formed in the rust, corrosion continues even when the article is moved to a clean atmosphere (Schikorr, 1941). The damage caused by sulphur dioxide to antiquities has been discussed by Thomson (1969).

In crevices the presence of sulphates can be very troublesome. The degree of hydration depends upon the humidity of the air and can be quite high e.g. $Na_2SO_4.1OH_2O$. If the atmosphere dries, the compound can break down and give cavities and absorbs more dissolved sulphates. The hydrate reforms and expands and so tends to produce local areas of high pressure and may even give malignant growths.

Chlorides

Chlorides in the atmosphere may originate from the sea or general industrial pollution. Many chlorides are hygroscopic so encourage electrochemical corrosion and also increase the conductivity of the solution. Because the chloride ion is small and relatively mobile it can easily diffuse to a metal surface and replace the protective and insoluble hydroxide ion with a soluble metal product so giving local attack such as pitting. Local areas containing high concentrations of ferrous chloride have been observed on iron (Feitknecht, 1952) as well as areas of high acidity in local crevices and pits.

Immersed corrosion

Many of the reactions which have been described above occur on iron and steel when it is immersed in fresh or sea water. The depth of immersion and the specific locality can affect the degree of aeration and the corrosion products. In sea water there is an ample supply of chloride ions and these are normally found in the corrosion products.

There are other ions, however, which may tend to form insoluble compounds and can reduce the rate of corrosion and these include magnesium and zinc (which can precipitate out as hydroxides) and calcium (which may give calcium carbonate). The initial rate of corrosion is very rapid, often about 0.13 $mm.y^{-1}$ in seawater, but decreases to a steady and much lower value.

Before attempting to use corrosion inhibitors to preserve iron artifacts it is beneficial to remove as much of the chloride ion as possible. Methods to do this have been described elsewhere (Oddy and Hughes, 1970; Urbon, 1970; Pearson, 1972; North and Pearson, 1974; Watkinson, 1974; Fenn and Foley, 1975) and tests devised to measure the efficiency of such methods (Semczak, 1977). The corrosion products formed on iron during marine corrosion and their stability have been discussed by North and Pearson (1977).

Undergound corrosion

The rate of corrosion is very dependent upon the conditions. The important factors include:–

1. the moisture content – very little corrosion in dry deserts.
2. the temperature – virtually no corrosion in the ice of the arctic and antarctic.
3. the acidity of the soil – little in a neutral environment
4. the presence of bacteria.

Thus weapons can often be found in dry or cold soils but not in very damp and hot tropical environments. Similarly in acidic peats which can be waterlogged the rate of corrosion is normally high.

Bacteria can accelerate the corrosion of iron by reducing sulphates – sulphate reducing bacteria. These can give rapid corrosion under normally safe conditions such as waterlogged clays in which there is no oxygen and the medium is neither acidic nor alkaline. According to Miller (1971), the reactions are:–

Dissociation of water
$$8H_2O \rightleftharpoons 8H^+ + 8(OH)^- \qquad (33)$$
Anodic reaction
$$4Fe \rightarrow 4Fe^{2+} + 8e \qquad (34)$$
Cathodic reaction
$$8H^+ + 8e \rightarrow 8H \qquad (35)$$
Bacteria involvement
$$SO_4^{2-} + 8H \rightarrow S^{2-} + 4H_2O \qquad (36)$$
Products
$$Fe^{2+} + S^{2-} \rightarrow FeS \qquad (37)$$
$$3Fe^{2+} + 6(OH)^- \rightarrow 3Fe(OH)_2 \qquad (38)$$
Overall
$$4Fe + SO_4^{2-} + 4H_2O \rightarrow$$
$$3Fe(OH)_2 + FeS + 2(OH)^- \qquad (39)$$

If oxygen is present it is possible for the ferrous sulphide to react:–
$$FeS + 2O_2 \rightarrow FeSO_4 \qquad (40)$$

This sulphate can then react as described above and produce sulphuric acid.

Corrosion inhibitors

According to Shreir (1965) "An inhibitor is a material which, when added in small amounts to an environment potentially corrosive to a metal or alloy in contact with it, effectively reduces the corrosion rate by diminishing the tendency of the metal or alloy to react with the environment".

There are several classifications of inhibitors including:–

1. anodic and cathodic inhibitors which preferentially reduce the anodic or cathodic reaction
2. non-oxidizing and oxidizing inhibitors which respectively do and do not require dissolved oxygen to be able to act to passivate the metal surface
3. safe and dangerous inhibitors which, if used at concentrations below the critical value, reduce the rate of corrosion to a low uniform rate (safe) or give localised intense corrosion or pitting (dangerous)
4. film forming and de-activating inhibitors
5. organic and inorganic inhibitors.

Anodic inhibitors

Many anionic species migrate to the anode and passivate the iron surface. Some of these are oxidizing agents which, in near neutral solutions, can operate with or without oxygen and include sodium nitrite and chromate:–

$$2Fe + NaNO_2 + 2H_2O \rightarrow$$
$$Fe_2O_3 + NaOH + NH_3 \qquad (41)$$
$$2Fe + 2Na_2CrO_4 + 2H_2O \rightarrow$$
$$Fe_2O_3 + Cr_2O_3 + 4NaOH. \qquad (42)$$

The difference between these is that the nitrite only produces an insoluble oxide whereas the chromate gives a film consisting of both ferric oxide and chromium oxide. These inhibitors are effective for iron at relatively low concentrations ($0.1gl^{-1}$). Other inhibitors can only function when dissolved oxygen is present. These include phosphates, borates, and benzoates and generally a higher concentration (10-15 gl^{-1} benzoate) is required.

The action of many of these inhibitors has been discussed by Lumsden and Szklarska – Smialowska (1978).

Cathodic inhibitors

Certain cations can act in neutral solutions and diffuse to the surface of the cathode and react with the hydroxyl ions produced to form insoluble precipitates which act as a barrier and slow the process. The important ions include calcium and magnesium, which can occur naturally in water, and zinc, nickel and manganese. The reactions include:–

$$Zn^{2+} + 2\,(OH)^- \rightarrow Zn\,(OH)_2 \downarrow \qquad\qquad (43)$$
and
$$Ca^{2+} + CO_2 + OH^- \rightarrow Ca(HCO_3)_2 \rightarrow CaCO_3 \downarrow \,(44)$$

Some metal ions such as arsenic or antimony may form a surface film on the cathode and reduce the cathodic hydrogen evolution process so these are particularly useful in acidic solutions.

Large colloidal cations such as polyphosphates $(Na_5CaP_6O_{18})_n^{n+}$ can also migrate to the cathode and form thick barrier films which inhibit the cathodic reaction.

Mixed inhibitors

Some chemicals such as zinc chromate can ionize in solution and affect both the anodic and cathodic reactions. Certain polyphosphates and silicates can also act by this mechanism.

Organic inhibitors

These are often used in acidic solutions such as pickling acids. Low molecular weight organic inhibitors are generally considered to be adsorbed on the metal surface. The inhibitive efficiency of amines has been found to increase with the chain length, the cross-sectional area of the molecule, the inclination of the molecule to the metal surface and other stereochemical properties (Mann, Lauer and Hultin, 1936). Polar organic compounds containing nitrogen, oxygen and sulphur can ionize in acids to give positively charged ammonium-, oxonium-, or sulphonium- type ions which are attracted to, and adsorbed at, the cathode areas so reducing the evolution of hydrogen.

Certain very large molecules such as gelatin, dextrin and agar are considered to adsorb on the metal surface. These compounds give a blanketing effect so increase the electrolyte resistance and reduce the corrosion current. They probably also reduce the rate of diffusion of reactants and products at the metal surface.

Safe and dangerous inhibitors

An inhibitor is considered to be safe if it uniformly lowers the total corrosion on the anodic surface. This is generally true for cathodic but not anodic inhibitors. Thus, if an insufficient concentration cathodic inhibitor is used, only part of the cathodic surface is covered and the rate of the reaction is reduced. This means that the corrosion current is reduced and less dissolution occurs at the anode; the distribution is not affected.

If there is insufficient anodic inhibitor present to cover the whole of the anodic surface then the dissolution can be concentrated at the uncovered exposed area. This can lead to local intense attack or pitting. In practice the concentration of an inhibitor can decrease due to adsorption on the metal surface, reaction with contaminants and leakage. Hence the initial concentration is generally much higher than that required for maintenance to ensure a sufficiently high amount of inhibitor in local crevices etc. The effect of chromate on the crevice corrosion on iron produced by chloride ions has been discussed by McCafferty et al (1977). They consider that for a given concentration of chloride ion there is a particular amount of chromate needed for inhibition. The chromate and chloride ions are considered to compete for adsorption on the surface.

Practical inhibition

A rough or dirty surface requires a higher concentration of inhibitor than is necessary for a clean surface. Hence it is advisable to clean an article before using corrosion inhibitors.

In general as the environment becomes more corrosive it is necessary to increase the concentration of an inhibitor. Thus it may be difficult to completely inhibit corrosion in high-chloride systems and a 10% solution of sodium nitrite may be necessary for steel in sea water. Alternatives include mixtures of inhibitors such as chromate with phosphate and dichromate with phosphate.

A mixture of different types of inhibitor may be synergistic and very beneficial. Thus a polyphosphate (cathodic) with a chromate (anodic) inhibitor has been advocated or an oxidizing agent (nitrite or chromate) with a non-oxidizing but precipitating chemical (orthophosphate or silicate).

The role of corrosion inhibitors in cleaning acids

Under certain circumstances acids are used to remove layers of corrosion products from metal artifacts. This practice is not normally recommended as the different chemicals that can be produced on the surface over the centuries may give valuable information about the life and use of the article.

Acids may also be used to remove the oxide scales formed during heating in the manufacture of iron articles. Thus one of the earliest examples of the use of inhibitors was the Middle Ages when master armourers used inhibited acids to clean armour. The acid dissolves the surface oxide so that the cleaned metal is exposed to corrosion and it is on these fresh surfaces that the inhibitor is preferentially adsorbed and protects them from attack by the acid. Thus the use of inhibitors reduces the corrosion of the exposed metal surface (often by up to 90%), minimises the consumption of acid and reduces the spray produced and possibly the uptake of hydrogen.

Chemicals which can be used as inhibitors or restrainers during pickling include amines, thioureas and aldehydes. The choice of inhibitor depends upon the metal and acid used and details are given in the literature (Uhlig, 1948; Every and Riggs, 1964; Riggs and Hurd, 1968).

It is sometimes beneficial to add a detergent or foaming agent to the pickling bath to help penetration of the acid into pores, crevices etc. as well as to reduce the spray. After removal from the bath the article is rinsed to remove the last traces of the acid. It may then be advantageous to dip the article into a mild alkaline, phosphate or chromate bath to prevent staining or corrosion during drying. An alternative procedure is a hot water rinse in a bath with a 35mm thick layer of stearic acid on the surface so that, when the article is removed from the solution, a water repellent film is left on the surface (Geld and D'Oria, 1967).

The role of corrosion inhibitors in reinforced concrete

Iron and steel are sometimes used to reinforce new or old statues and buildings. Thus the back of some of the statues on top of St. Paul's Cathedral, London have iron supports behind them. Some concretes contain chemicals such as calcium chloride to accelerate the setting of the concrete. When this concrete gets wet the chloride ions can diffuse to the iron and cause corrosion producing voluminous corrosion products. These give the surrounding areas a rusty appearance and cause breaking of the concrete or surrounding stone due to the local internal stresses.

Hence if iron is to be used for reinforcement it is strongly recommended that suitable corrosion inhibitors are added to the concrete (Anon, 1975a; Hildebrand, 1976). These inhibitors include calcium nitrite (Ostrovskii, Norgorodskii and Ratinov, 1975; Lundquist, Rosenberg and Gaidis, 1979), sodium benzoate or nitrite and calcium lignosulphonate (Anon, 1975b). The nitrite ion is considered to oxidise the ferrous ions to ferric ions which block the diffusion of ferrous ions from the iron.

Corrosion in show cases and boxes

Before discussing the use of volatile corrosion inhibitors in storage and packaging it is useful to consider the factors which affect this form of corrosion. Atmospheric corrosion can be increased by:–

1. oxygen in the air
2. water vapour
3 the presence of stimulating species such as hygroscopic compounds, sweat residues, dust and acidic vapours.

Although the removal of oxygen from an enclosed space is very unusual, Barton (1976), has quoted a museum which replaced the air by an inert gas in a closed chamber containing delicate or valuable objects. The removal of the air must be complete because as little as 3% oxygen in the gaseous environment can give corrosion.

The removal of water vapour is much simpler and cheaper. If the relative humidity is maintained below about 60% very little corrosion of steel occurs. This may be achieved by the use of desiccants such as silica gel in the storage or display case. Alternatively it may be possible to maintain a uniform temperature to prevent condensation or to keep the article warm. The use of dehumidifying equipment for the preservation of weapons and armour in museums has been described by Bailey (1978). The control of humidity and air pollution in show cases has been discussed by Padfield (1966) and McQueen (1979).

If possible it is beneficial to filter air entering a room or show case to remove air-borne particles. Vernon (1943, 1948-49), in his classical work on this subject, has shown that some of these particles can promote rusting of iron surfaces. Show cases or boxes for storing or transporting articles are often made of wood. As these have little or no ventilation it is possible that moisture and vapours may become concentrated inside and corrosion can occur. This is particularly true for freshly felled timber, acidic woods or boxes exposed to rain. Vapours produced by wood used for show cases or in packaging can be very acidic and cause corrosion (Farmer, 1962). The emission of these vapours (Arni, Cochrane and Gray, 1965) and the resulting corrosion (Budd, 1965) have been described elsewhere. As little as 0.5ppm acetic acid can promote the corrosion of metals (Clarke and Longhurst, 1961) and at 48°C as much as 7% of the original weight of oak wood can be released as acetic acid over a period of two years (Budd, 1965). Attack may also result from vapours produced by air-drying paints, varnishes, glues in plywood and joints, plastic fittings and fabric linings.

If these corrosive conditions can be avoided the tendency for corrosion is greatly reduced. Thus the use of impervious linings such as aluminium can be used to prevent the entry of acidic vapours. Thick polyetheylene is also used and it should be heat sealed or zipped and preferably desiccated inside. Further protection can be obtained by the use of volatile corrosion inhibitors.

Volatile corrosion inhibitors

Certain corrosion inhibitors are volatile so do not need to be applied directly to the metal surface. They are generally used in enclosed systems such as show cases, pianos, tool boxes and inside waxed paper packaging.

Most of these chemicals for use with ferrous

metals are amine nitrites, benzoates or chromates. The active components are oxidizing anions such as nitrites or groups which act by adsorption such as benzoates and they reinforce any existing oxide film on the metal surface. The amines probably dissolve in any moisture present and tend to prevent acidic conditions as well as oxidizing any exposed areas on the iron surface. In order to vapourize they are combined with compounds with a relatively high vapour pressure at room temperature.

Among the best of these inhibitors for iron are dicyclohexylamine nitrite and cyclohexylamine carbonate. These are available as powders and in impregnated wrapping papers and bags.

Ideally the inhibitors should be used with clean metal surfaces so that good film adherence is possible. This also reduces the chance of local cells forming underneath the film in local recesses etc. Initially a high concentration of inhibitor is used to build the surface film as rapidly as possible. The concentration can be reduced to a maintenance level sufficient to repair breaks in the protective surface film caused by mechanical or chemical damage.

Application of the inhibitors to the cleaned artifacts may be by immersing, swabbing or spraying with a 5% w/v solution in a non-aqueous solvent such as methylated spirits. Immersion by dipping is best because it ensures complete coverage if the articles are moved or rotated to allow air bubbles etc to escape from recesses. Storage in a container with the volatile inhibitor should then ensure lasting protection.

It should be noted that certain inhibitors are specific and protect iron or steel but may cause corrosion on other metals such as zinc. Hence articles made of more than one metal or containing inlaid decorations should be treated with particular care.

Details on the materials and methods involved in the use of volatile corrosion inhibitors are given elsewhere (Lee, Seno and Asahara, 1974; Miksic, 1977; Day, 1978; Rengivivh, 1978; Heidemann, 1979; Trabarelli and Zucchi, 1979).

Inhibitors in the preservation of antiques

In the preservation of antiques the integrity of the object is important and any process performed should, ideally, be reversible.

Many iron objects that are recovered have a loose coating of rust covering any remaining metal. The cleaning of the article depends upon its condition and the amount of metal left. Several approaches are possible in the preservation of iron.

Complete stripping of the corrosion products using oxalic or thioglycollic acid containing a suitable inhibitor may be necessary. The article can then be impregnated in a paraffin bath at 130°C and coated with a wax mixed with soot or dried in air to give a flash coating of rust and blackened with tannin (Stambolov, 1979). Methods for the protection of cleaned iron objects have been discussed by Biek, Cripps and Thacker (1954). Western (1972), has used wax or lacquer to conserve excavated iron objects after cleaning. The use of poly-phosphate complexes as corrosion inhibitors has been advocated by Pelikán (1964) for derusted iron articles such as firearms.

If heavy rusting and corrosion has occurred it is probably not advisable to remove the surface layer. It is necessary, however, to stabilise the corrosion products and the presence of chloride ions is particularly important. Several papers have been written on this topic and details can be obtained from the literature (Oddy and Hughes, 1970; Urbon, 1970; Pearson, 1972; North and Pearson, 1974; Watkinson, 1974; Fenn and Foley, 1975). Once the chloride has been removed the article, such as a cannon, can be washed, dried and covered with a microcrystalline wax (Pearson, 1972) or a coating of 'Ebonide' (Rees-Jones, 1972). It may be possible to stabilise the rust with a combination of inhibitors such as phosphoric acid containing tannin (Fenn and Foley, 1975) although some tannin treatments have not been successful (Stambolov, 1979). The use of tannin as a corrosion inhibitor for iron has been discussed in some detail by Pelikán (1964) and by Gust and Wieczorek (1978). A rather unusual approach to the stabilisation process is suggested by Stambolov (1979), who used a water repellent chemical, methyl triethoxy silane. The porous layers treated are insensitive in both water and water vapour (Weber, 1975).

The final method involves the in-situ reduction of the metal compounds back to the metal. This is difficult but can be attempted by consolidative reduction involving electrolyses as described by Plenderleith and Werner (1971).

There are many scientific papers covering the inhibition of corrosion of mild steel in sea-water. Some of these chemicals, however, leave surface films of compounds which may be misleading to future investigators. It may be possible to remove organic inhibitors more easily than inorganic inhibitors. Thus straight chain amines (Fujii and Aramaki, 1960) with C_{16} or C_{18} have been found to give about 80% inhibition with a concentration of 100 to 200 ppm for steel in sea-water. Triphenyl benzyl phosphonium chloride (Sanyal and Srivastava, 1974), an onium compound, can give 85% inhibition to mild steel in concentrated hydrochloric acid so it should be a good inhibitor in other aggressive environments. It is claimed to affect the anodic and cathodic processes and with potassium iodide acts synergistically. The use of chromates, which leave a film of chromium oxide on the surface, has already been discussed. Golden and Mayne (1978) have shown that zinc potassium chromate is better than potassium chromate for sea water containing chloride and sulphate ions: the zinc salt acts as a cathodic as well as an anodic inhibitor. A combination (Balezin and Kemkhadze, 1968) of chromate and nitrite (10000 ppm) or nitrite and benzoate (15000 ppm) is claimed to give almost complete protection to carbon steel in sea-water. Zinc gluconate (Mor and Wrubl, 1976) is claimed to completely protect steel from corrosion in stagnant sea-water when a concentration of 500 ppm is used. The zinc again gives a precipitation of hydroxide and possibly carbonate at the cathode so stops diffusion of oxygen to the cathode and some anodic inhibition occurs. The addition of surface active substances (surfactants) to solutions of inhibitors has been shown to increase the effectiveness (Petukhova, Gregor'eva and Shtan'ko, 1975).

Care must be taken before subjecting priceless articles to unproven inhibitive solutions. It may be worth using the above inhibiting compounds to treat iron articles after the removal of soil etc. This procedure may well stabilize the aggressive ions so that the treated objects can be safely displayed in dry show cases.

Another role of corrosion inhibitors is an addition to waxes, oils, lacquers and paints so that additional protection may be afforded. This can be important at gaps in a coating when moisture can reach the surface and leach out the inhibitor from the surface coating. This, together with dry atmospheres and volatile corrosion, inhibitors, should increase the protection of cleaned, stabilized iron artifacts.

References

Anon, a., Corrosion inhibiting admixtures. *Materials Performance.* 14 (1) 1975, p.38,.

Anon, b., Guide to use of admixtures in concrete. *Materials Performance.* 14 (1) 1975, p.38.

Arni, P.C., Cochrane, G.C. and Gray, J.D., The emission of corrosive vapours by wood. *Journal of Applied Chemistry.* 15 1965, p.305 and 463.

Bailey, P.M., Corrosion prevention by humidity control. *Product Finishing.* 31 (6) 1978, p.18.

Balezin, S.A. and Kemkhadze, T.V., *2nd International Congress of Marine Corrosion Fouling, Athens,* 1968, p.31.

Barton, K., Principles of protection against atmospheric corrosion. *Protection Against Atmospheric Corrosion.* J. Wiley, London. 1976. p.87.

Biek, L., Cripps, E.S. and Thacker, D.M.D., Some method for protecting cleaned iron objects. *Museums Journal.* 54 1954, p.32.

Budd, M.K., Corrosion of metals in association with wood. *Applied Materials Research.* 4 (2) 1965, p.124.

Clarke, S.G. and Longhurst, E.E., The corrosion of metals by acid vapours from wood. *Journal of Applied Chemistry.* 11 1961, p.435.

Day, F.T., Packaging to control corrosion, rust, fire hazards etc. *Product Finishing.* 31 (5) 1978, p.11.

Every, R.L. and Riggs, O.L., Organic inhibitors for carbon steel in hydrochloric acid. *Materials Protection.* 3 (9) 1964, p.46.

Farmer, R.H., Corrosion of metals in association with wood. *Wood.* 27 1962, pp.326 and 443.

Feitknecht, W., The breakdown of the oxide film on metal surfaces in acid vapours and the mechanism of atmospheric corrosion. *Chimia.* 6 1952, p.3.

Fenn, J.D. and Foley, K., Passivation of Iron. *Conservation in Archaeology and the Applied Arts. Stockholm Congress.* 1975, pp.195-198.

Fujii, S. and Aramaki, K., *1st European Symposium of Corrosion Inhibition, Ferrara, Italy,* 1960, p.215.

Geld, I. and D'Oria, F., Post-pickle rust inhibitors. *Materials Protection.* 6 (8) 1967, p.42.

Golden, J. and Mayne, J.E.O., Inhibition of the corrosion of mild steel by zinc potassium chromate. *British Corrosion Journal.* 13 1978, p.45.

Gust, J. and Wieczorek, C., Preparations based on tannin or tanning agents for rust stabilization. *Ochr. Przea. Korozja.* 21 1978, p.256.

Heidemann, G., Corrosion protection through VCI paper. *Anti-Corrosion.* 26 (11) 1979, p.5.

Hildebrand, J.F., Evaluation of corrosion inhibiting compounds for the protection of pre-stressing systems. *Institute of Mechanical Engineers.* 1976, p.245.

Lee, B.S. Seno, M. and Asahara, T., Effects of various sub-components and reducing agents on rust inhibiting action of hexamethylenetetramine for iron. *Journal of the Metal Finish Society. Japan.* 25 (7) 1974, p.392.

Lumsden, J.B. and Szklarska-Smialowska, Z. The properties of films formed on iron exposed to inhibitive solutions. *Corrosion.* 34 (5) 1978, p.8.

Lundguist, J.T., Rosenberg, A.M. and Gaidis, J.M., Calcium nitrite as an inhibitor of rebar corrosion in chloride containing concrete. *Materials Performance.* 18 (3) 1979, p.36.

Mann, C.A., Lauer, B.E. and Hultin, C.T., Organic inhibitors of corrosion. *Industrial Engineering Chemistry.* 28 1936, pp.159 and 1048.

McCafferty, E. *et al.,* Effect of chromate ion on the crevice corrosion of iron. *Journal of the Electrochemical Society Conference,* 1977, Abstract No. 122.

McQueen, M., Display and storage of metal objects after conservation. *Conservation and Restoration of Metals Symposium, Edinburgh,* 1979, p.70.

Miksic, B.A., Volatile corrosion inhibitors. *Journal of the Electrochemical Society Conference,* 1977, Abstract No. 120.

Miller, J.D.A., Microbial corrosion of buried and immersed metal. *Microbial Aspects of Metallury.* MTP Co Ltd., Aylesbury, England. 1971, p.73.

Mor, E.D. and Wrubl, C., Zinc gluconate as an inhibitor of the corrosion of mild steel in sea-water. *British Corrosion Journal.* 11 1976, p.199.

North, N.A. and Pearson, C., Thermal decomposition of FeOC1 and marine cast iron corrosion products. *Studies in Conservation.* 22 1977, pp.146-157.

North, N.A. and Pearson, C., Washing methods for chloride removal from marine iron artifacts. *Studies in Conservation.* 23 1978, pp.174-186.

Oddy, W.A. and Hughes, M.J., Stabilisation of 'active' bronze and iron antiquities by the use of sodium sesquicarbonate. *Studies in Conservation.* 15 1970, pp.183-189.

Ostrovskii, A.B., Norgorodskii, V.I. and Ratinov, V.B., Increasing the protective properties of concrete with respect to steel reinforcements. *Protection Metals.* 11 (1) 1975, p.73.

Padfield, T., Control of relative humidity and air pollution in show-cases and picture frames. *Studies in Conservation.* 11 1966, pp.8-30.

Pearson, C., The preservation of iron cannon after 200 years under the sea. *Studies in Conservation.* 17 1972, pp.91-110.

Pelikán, J.B., The use of polyphosphate complexes in conservation of iron or steel objects. *Studies in Conservation.* 9 1964, p.59.

Pelikán, J.B., Conservation of iron with tannin. *Studies in Conservation.* 11 1966, pp.109-116.

Petukhova, G.S., Gregor'eva, G.S. and Shtan'ko, V.M., Protection of ferrous metals from atmospheric corrosion by wetting with solutions of inhibitors with surfactant additives. *Protection Metals.* 11 (1) 1975, p.70.

Plenderleith, H.J. and Werner, A.E.A., *The Conservation of Antiquities and Works of Art.* 2nd Ed. 1971. Oxford University Press, London.

Rees-Jones, S.G., Some aspects of conservation of iron objects recovered from the sea. *Studies in Conservation.* 17 1972, pp.39-43.

Rengivivh, E.N., Anti-corrosion packaging papers. *Przeglad Papier. 33 (6)* 1978, p.214.

Riggs, O.L. and Hurd, R.M., Effects of inhibitors on scale removed in HC1 pickling solutions. *Corrosion. 24 (2)* 1968, p.45.

Sanyal, B. and Srivastava, K., Inhibitive effect of an onium compound on the dissolution of steel in hydrochloric acid. *British Corrosion Journal. 9* 1974, p.103.

Schikorr, G., Atmospheric rusting of iron. *Korrosion un Metallschutz. 17 1941, p.305.*

Schikorr, G., Mechanism of the atmospheric corrosion of iron. *Werkstoffe und Korrosion. 14* 1963, p.69.

Semczak, C.M., A comparison of chloride tests. *Studies in Conservation. 22* 1977, pp.40-41.

Shreir, L.L., Corrosion inhibition: Principles and practice. *Corrosion.* Vol.2. 1965. G. Newnes, London. pp.12.18.

Stambolov, T., Introduction to the conservation of ferrous and non-ferrous metals. *Conservation and Restoration of Metals Symposium, Edinburgh,* 1979, p.10.

Thomson, G. Sulphur dioxide damage to antiquities. Comments. *Atmospheric Environment. 3 (6)* 1969, p.687.

Trabarelli, G. and Zucchi, F., Fundamentals of inhibition with V.C.I.'s. *Corrosion '79, NACE Conference,* Houston, Texas, U.S.A Paper No. 82.

Uhlig, H.H., Inhibitors and passivators. *The Corrosion Handbook.* 1948. J. Wiley and Son Inc. p.910.

Urbon, B., The new conservation studies of the museum of the province of Württemberg. *Studies in Conservation. 15* 1970, pp.225-230.

Vernon, W.H.J., The corrosion of metals in air. Chemistry and Industry. 1943, p.314; *Journal of the Royal Society of Arts. 97* 1948-49, pp.578 and 593.

Watkinson, D., Lithium hydroxide – an interim report. *Conservation and Restoration of Metals Symposium, Edinburgh,* 1974, p.24.

Weber, H., Stone renovation and consolidation using silicones and silinic esters. *Proceedings of the International Symposium, Bologna,* 1975, p.375.

Western, A.C., The conservation of excavated iron objects. *Studies in Conservation. 17* 1972, pp.83-87.

Wrangler, G., *An Introduction to Corrosion and Protection of Metals.* 1972. Butler and Tanner Ltd. London.

DISCUSSION

Chairman:

D. Leigh

L. Biek
Electro-coating, wet or dry, depends on the conductivity of your artifact. How do you make magnetite coated objects conductive?

M.W. Pascoe
It is usually used on objects that are not too heavily oxidised. There is enough conductivity, certainly in phosphate coatings, to give an effective result. You can get very good deposits of coagulated polymer within about three minutes. At a stoving temperature of about 150°C film thicknesses of $25\mu m$ can be cured after approximately 30 minutes. There are both anodic and cathodic processes currently available.

B. Knight
Because the vapour phase inhibitors are nitrite salts of amines is there an possibility of nitrosamines being formed which could be dangerous?

R. Walker
I have not had any problems in that particular area. The particular compound is in fact produced by Shell Chemicals who I'm sure would have looked into this. In general one is thinking of using the inhibitor in a sealed container.

M.W. Pascoe
There are carbonates as well.

R. Walker
Yes there are carbonates but these are not quite as good as the nitrites.

S. Turgoose
What do you think the chances are of the inhibitors reaching the actual metal surface?

R. Walker
That very much depends on the physical form present. Assuming there are crevices, and these are the areas where there is the greatest problem, the surface is rough and porous and you therefore need a much higher concentration. When treating bronze with benzotriazol you can try evacuating the system to draw out the air in the corrosion products and hopefully replace it with fresh solution right down to the metal surface. The fact that there is liquid present however makes it more difficult for something else to come in and compete. There is evidence that the chromate ion has to compete with the chloride ion for adsorption onto the metal surface; if there is enough chromate it will work, if there is not enough chromate there it will not. How you actually determine the concentration at the surface without destroying the surface film is a problem.

S. Turgoose
Are you going to get crevice corrosion underneath inert particles such as sand grains, which are attached to the surface and which you cannot do anything about?

R. Walker
No, the fact that water has got under there in the first place means that if you can increase the migration of the particular inhibitor it will work.

S. Turgoose
But there is going to be a difference across the surface?

R. Walker
Yes of course and that is why you need more of the inhibitor. I don't know whether you can use something like ultrasonic cleaning or ultrasonic agitation to help speed the diffusion of the ions through to the metal surface. This is done in cleaning for industrial purposes and in electroplating. Warming the object up will again speed up the diffusion process but whether the inhibitor will get to the bottom of the crevices is an open question.

J. Price
For objects that have copper on, do you think the amines would be beneficial or injurious to the copper?

R. Walker
That is a problem because many of the inhibitors are very specific. Some of the amines for instance will be beneficial for iron but will attack zinc. Benzotriazole plus an amine may be suitable as you might in fact get a synergystic effect whereby two inhibitors working together will give a better result than either by itself. Theoretically it should work.

D. Barker
I did try that experiment and you get corrosion of the copper.

B. Knight
How much does it matter whether you can or cannot get the inhibitor right to the metal core beneath a centimetre or so of magnetite? Because if you could inhibit the cathodic reaction it would not matter too much about getting to the surface but you would need a very efficient cathodic inhibitor.

R. Walker
That would be a possibility. Following on from that, if the water has to diffuse through cracks in the magnetite you are forming a precipitate on the magnetite. With the cathodic inhibitors you might in fact block the pores through which the water would diffuse inwards and the ferrous ions would have to diffuse outwards, so you might inhibit corrosion in a round about way. I would strongly recommend the cathodic inhibitors because they are safer.

D. Barker
In that case where is the cathode going to be; are you saying it is on top of the magnetite because it's not going to be along the metal surface?

R. Walker
It may well be on the magnetite, the anodic surface would be underneath where the metal is.

S. Turgoose

The question is whether these things effectively inhibit the cathodic reaction on the magnetite?

R. Walker

Yes that is so. On the other hand if they form a precipitate on the surface of the magnetite they will block the diffusion of oxygen through to the metal surface.

FINAL DISCUSSION

Chairman:
M. W. Pascoe

R. Lewendon

I think it is a pity that methods of quantifying the rates of corrosion have not been covered today. From a management point of view this is very important because these processes cost money. What we are doing at the Royal Artillery Institution, in conjunction with City University, is to try and quantify the rate at which our *Mary Rose* cannon is rusting away. I'm hopeful that in one or two years time we will be able to say by how much per year the corrosion is progressing. I would make the plea however that more research time be devoted to similar quantitative methodology.

D. Barker

Corrosion rates for a wide variety of environments are well documented in the appropriate literature. The average rate of corrosion in a rural environment is 25 to 30μm per year. In a marine environment it is approximately 80 to 90μm per year and in an industrial environment I would imagine it is over 100μm per year. These figures are for linear corrosion rates but in actual fact it is a parabolic relationship and the curve does start to tail off. It is not really known how long it takes for the tailing off to occur because corrosion rates have not been observed continuously over long periods of say 50 to 70 years. Short term investigations of 5 to 15 years only have been carried out.

R. Boff

I would like to point out that the corrosion rate will appear parabolic as long as you have a nice coherent oxide layer. As soon as this layer flakes or cracks then oxygen has direct access and you are back to your initial rate of corrosion.

D. Barker

Most workers record a linear relationship. How do you propose to quantify this work at City University?

R. Lewendon

I cannot provide you with the technical details. We were advised to contact City University where they are pioneering this photogrammetric methodolgy on buildings and it seemed possible that this could be a applied to other massive objects.

L. Biek

You will need rigidity in your supporting base if you are to detect any movement.

R. Lewendon

During the initial examination rigid reference points were put into the floor of the museum from which all the photographs will be referred back to.

L. Biek

It is the change in the relative positions of the various parts of the surface providing a sort of contouring effect; comparison could be done automatically using computerised machines. One further

point. It was suggested earlier that as soon as objects come out of the ground they should be put into alkaline sulphite until we are ready to deal with them. I would agree with this statement. While the objects are in alkaline sulphite solution they can be taken out to be X-rayed, drawn, photographed etc, and then put back again until such time we are able to clean them, stablize them or conserve them. Furthermore, the storage method requires very little maintenance.

M. Brooks

Concerning alkaline sulphite: I would not recommend putting all iron objects direct from excavation into the solution without prior examination. This was done with some iron which had very little metal core and when taken out of the solution it was extremely fragile and very difficult to clean.

S. Blackshaw

If you weigh the objects when they are excavated it may provide some indication of whether or not you have any metal core left. The weighing would also provide some idea of the extent of mineralization. If this was total there would be no rusting and you would not need to stablize it in alkaline sulphite.

B. Knight

You would still need to keep it damp to prevent it from drying out.

S. Blackshaw

I have been told by some excavators that they have never experienced that problem.

B. Knight

It varies from site to site, in some sites the objects are in a terrible condition in a comparatively short time and in others it may take a couple of years.

S. Blackshaw

But there is still no ideal solution to storing it. Whether you store them wet or dry you are not going to exclude oxygen – even vacuum packs are still permeable.

M.W. Pascoe

This is so unless I think you have aluminium foil inside. Metal foils, unless they are punctured, should be the most impervious coatings you can find. All the organic coatings, even if they are crystalline, will be permeable.

B. Knight

One hopes, in theory at least, that the period between excavation and treatment is going to be, at the most, two years and that we could keep the oxygen out for that period until the conservation is completed.

R. Boff

I believe diffusion through low density polythene occurs in weeks rather than years?

M. W. Pascoe

Diffusion can occur fairly quickly particularly through the non-crystalline regions. There is considerable crystallinity as in some waxes but there are also regions which oxygen and sometimes water vapour can pass through.

J. Cronyn

What about storing iron by deep-freezing? I believe this has been done in Scandinavia. Has anybody any experience of iron which has been stored in this way?

Anon

If you include the material from the frozen tombs in Russia which was accidently frozen in the permafrost then that is in very good condition.

L. Biek

That is freezing before deterioration has commenced, we are concerned with objects where deterioration is well advanced.

S. Keene

I have some nails stored in a domestic deep freezer and at the moment I can only say that they have not instantly disintegrated.

M. W. Pascoe

The difficulty with cooling systems is of course that as soon as you remove the object you get condensation and the object becomes damp.

M. Loynd

I can see some confusion developing as to how we should actually store our iron objects. We have gone through the desalination arguments and discussions on whether the object should be kept wet or dry. Is Dr. Knight proposing that we keep the objects wet in perpetuity or is he proposing some substitute for the water and therefore prevent shrinkage at the time of treatment?

B. Knight

We cannot expect to keep the object wet indefinitely. What we can do is to control the drying out. I do not yet know how slowly this drying needs to be or indeed whether we can put anything into the pores to minimise the shrinkage.

M. Loynd

I am concerned as to whether we can get some parameters at an early stage. The problem with a symposium like this is that knowledge is dissipated in a diluted and understated form; people act on this information occasionally with disastrous results. Now that we have the concepts some work should be done quickly to bring it to a satisfactory conclusion.

B. Knight

I agree entirely. We must do what we can to prevent people from putting things into buckets of water and expecting them to be conserved.

J. Price

Could I add to that that the concept of silica gel storage would still hold for treated material. You would still store things in as dry an atmosphere as possible.

List of participants

ADAMS, Miss B.   Victoria and Albert Museum, London SW7 2RL
AKED, Mr. S.   Portsmouth City Museum
ANTONIO, Mrs. K.M.   Ancient Monuments Lab., Rm 4, 17 Atholl Crescent, Edinburgh EH3 8JN
ASHLEY-SMITH, Dr. J.   Victoria and Albert Museum, London SW7 2RL
ATKINSON, Mr. J.W.J.   North of England Museums Service, 25 Harvey Close, Crowther Estate, Washington, Tyne and Wear

BACON, Miss A.L.   Saffron Walden Museum, Saffron Walden, Essex
BARKER, Dr. D.   Dept. of Chemistry, Portsmouth Polytechnic, White Swan Road, Portsmouth, Hants PO1 2ST
BARKER, Ms. S.C.   Horniman Museum, London Road, Forest Hill, London SE23
BAYLY, Sir P.V..   The Maritime Trust, 16 Ebury Street, London SW1
BIEK, Mr. L.   Ancient Monuments Laboratory, DOE, 23 Savile Row, London W1X 2AA
BILLINGS, Miss P.   National Maritime Museum, Greenwich, London
BIRNIE, Mr. L.A.A.   National Maritime Museum, Greenwich, London
BLACK, Mr. J.   Institute of Archaeology, 31-34 Gordon Square, London WC1H 0PY
BLACKSHAW, Mrs. S.   Dept. of Conservation & Technical Services, British Museum, London WC1B 3DG
BOFF, Dr. R.M.   British Museum, London
BROOKS, Miss M A.   Brewhouse Yard Museum, Castle Boulevard, Nottingham
BRYCE, Mr. T.   National Museum of Antiquities of Scotland, Conservation & Research Laboratories, Govt. Training Centre Complex, West Granton Road, Edinburgh EH5 1JA

CALNAN, Mr. C.N.   Castle Museum, Norwich
CAMERON, Mr. E.A.   Kent Museums Service, Education Dept., West Malling Air Station, Nr. Maidstone, Kent
CAMPBELL, Mr. N.J.M.   Quarhurst, Binstead, Ryde, Isle of Wight
CAPLE, Mr. C.   Dept. of Archaeological Sciences, University of Bradford, Bradford, West Yorks BD7 1DP.
CLARKE, Mr. D.   Ministry of Defence (PE), Qual Assce Directorate (Ordinance), Training Centre Buildings 43, Royal Arsenal West, Woolwich SE18
CLARKE, Dr. R.W.   National Maritime Museum, Greenwich, London
CLIFFORD, Mrs. B.   National Maritime Museum, Greenwich, London
COLE, Mr. R N.   Science Division, Butterworth & Co (Publishers) Ltd., Borough Green, Sevenoaks, Kent TN15 8PH
COOK, Miss A.M..   105 Cunningham Close, Shoeburyness, Essex
CORFIELD, Mr. M.C..   Wiltshire County Council, Library & Museum Service, Bythesea Road, Trowbridge, Wilts
CRONYN, Miss J.   Dept. of Archaeology, University of Durham, 46 Sadler Street, Durham

DANIELS, Dr. V.   British Museum, London
DAVID, Mr. A.E.   North Western Museum and Art Gallery Service, Griffin Lodge, Griffin Park, Cavendish Place, Blackburn, BB2 2PN
DEL RE, Ms. C.   Institute of Archaeology, London
DOVE, Ms. S.   British Museum, London

EDGE, Mr. D.A.   The Wallace Collection, Manchester Sq., London W1
EDWARDS, Dr. B.P.   City of Bristol Museum and Art Gallery, Queens Rd., Bristol
ENDERLEY, Miss R.C.   British Museum, London

FELL, Mrs. V.   Durham University
FERGUSON, Mr. F.   RAM Museum, Queen Street, Exeter
FISHER, Miss P.   British Museum, London
FLETCHER, Mr. M.A.   Ironbridge Gorge Museum Trust Ltd., The Wharfage, Ironbridge, Telford, Salop TF3 4AL

FOLEY, Miss K.	Lincoln Archaeological Trust, The Sessions House, Lindum Road, Lincoln LN2 1PB
FUSSELL, Ms. A.	CM 244, Dept of Civil Engineering, The City University, Northampton Square, London EC1
GANIARIS, Ms. H.	Museum of London, London Wall, London EC2Y 5HN
GOLDSTRAW, Miss R.	British Museum, London
GOWING, Mr. C.N.	Buckingham County Museum, Church Street, Aylesbury, Bucks HP20 2QP
GREENHILL, Mr. B.	National Maritime Museum, Greenwich, London
GREGSON, Mr. C.W.	National Maritime Museum, Greenwich, London
HÅFORS, Ms. B..	Statens Sjöhistoriska Museum, Konserveringstekniska avd, Djurgardsbrunnsvägen 24, 115 27 Stockholm, Sweden
HARRIS, Mr. R.	Victoria and Albert Museum, London
HAWARDEN, Miss H.M.	Windermere Steamboat Museum, Rayrigg Road, Windermere, Cumbria
HAYWOOD, Mr. C.	23 Doonanore Park, Dun Laoghaire, Co Dublin, Eire
HAZLE, Mr. J.R.	Royal Scottish Museum, Chambers Street, Edinburgh
HIBBERD, Mr. M.G.	Imperial War Museum, Dept. of Exhibits & Firearms, Lambeth Road, London SE1
HOCKEY, Miss M.	British Museum, London
HOLMES, Mr. R.	British Museum, London
HORSLEY, Miss J.M.	National Maritime Museum, Greenwich, London
HOWES, Mr. K.	British Museum, London
HUGGINS, Mr. P.J.	27 Grange Court, Waltham Abbey, Essex
HUGHES, Maj. Gen. B.P.	Royal Artillery Institution, Old Royal Military Academy, Woolwich Common, London SE18 4JJ
HUTCHINSON, Mr. B.	National Maritime Museum, Greenwich, London.
JACKSON, Miss P.	British Museum, London
JANAWAY, Mr. R.C.	Dept. of Archaeology, Leeds University LS2 9JT
JOEL, Mr. F.W.	Frank W. Joel Ltd., PO Box 6, Downham Market, Norfolk
JOHNSON, Ms. R.I.	Inverness Museum & Art Gallery, Castle Wynd, Inverness IV2 3ED
JURLEFF, Miss G.	Institute of Archaeology, London
KEENE, Ms. S.V.	Museum of London, London Wall, EC2Y 5HN
KENDELL, Mr. K.	Dept. of Chemistry, Portsmouth Polytechnic, White Swan Road, Portsmouth, Hants PO1 2ST
KENNEDY, Mr. R.A.	Pembroke Museums, The Castle, Haverfordwest, Dyfed SA61 2EG
KNIGHT, Dr. B.	Ancient Monuments Laboratory, London
LANE, Mrs. H.	British Museum, London
LANGFORD, Ms. S.	Southampton Archaeological Research Committee, 25a Oxford Street, Southampton
LEIGH, Dr. D.	Dept. of Archaeology, University Co., PO Box 78, Cardiff
LEWENDON, Brig. R.J.	Royal Artillery Institution, Woolwich
LOYND, Mr. M.W.	Yorks and Humberside Museum and Art Gallery Service
MARSDEN, Ms. F.J.	Museum of Sussex Archaeology, Barbican House, High Street, Lewes
MacGREGOR, Mr. C.	Durham University
McCANN, Mr. C.V.	Imperial War Museum, London
McCARTHY, Mr. C.K.	Imperial War Museum, London
McDONNELL, Mr. J.G.	Dept. of Metallurgy & Materials, Univ. of Aston in Birmingham, Gosta Green, Birmingham 4
McGRAIL, Dr. S.	National Maritime Museum, Greenwich, London
McINTYRE, Mr. I.	British Museum, London
MARSDEN, Ms. F.J.	Museum of Sussex Archaeology, Barbican House, High Street, Lewes, E. Sussex BN7 1YE
MARSH, Ms. D.M.	Huntly House Museum, 142 Canongate, Edinburgh ER1 2PA
MARTIN, Mr. R.	Conservation Dept., Royal Pavilion, Art Gallery & Museums, Brighton, East Sussex BN1 1UE

MASKELYNE, Mr. R.J.	Chichester Civic Society, Excavations Committee, 6 Crane Street, Chichester, Sussex
MATTHEWS, Mrs. L.M.	Lanchashire County Museums Service, Stanley Street, Preston, PR1 4YP
MELVILLE, Mr. B.J.	The Royal Scottish Museum, Chambers St., Edinburgh
MITCHELL, Mr. G.	Manx Museum, Douglas Isle of Man
MOORE, Mr. W.F.	Committee for Underwater Archaeology, 27 High Street, Shaftesbury, Dorset SP7 8JE
MORGAN, Mr. K.B.L.	North Western Museum & Art Gallery Service, Blackburn
MUCKLEROY, Mr. K.M.	National Maritime Museum, Greenwich, London
MUSTY, Mr. J.W.G.	Ancient Monuments Lab., DOE, London
NEWEY, Miss H.	British Museum, London
NORMAN, Miss K.	British Museum, London
O'CONNOR, Mrs. S.A.	Dept. of Archaeology, University College, Cardiff
O'SHEA, Mr. C.	Portsmouth Museum, Dept. of Conservation, 11 French St., Old Portsmouth, Hants PO1 2JS
OLDFIELD, Mrs. E.A.	Pyt House, W. Lavington, Nr. Devizes, Wilts.
PARISH, Mr. D.A.	Buckinghamshire County Museum, Church Street, Aylesbury, Bucks. HP20 2QP
PARROTT, M.K.	Museum of London, London Wall, EC2Y 5HN
PASCOE, Dr. M.W.	British Museum, London
PEARCE, Miss P.M.	British Museum, London.
PRICE, Mr. J.G.	Ancient Monuments Lab., DOE, London
REID, Mr. R.J.	Proof and Experimental Establishment, New Range, Shoeburyness, Southend, Essex
RINUY, Ms. A.	Laboratoire du Musee d'Art et d'Histoire, 9-11 Rue du Clos, 1207, Geneva
ROBERTS, Miss M.E.	Littlecote Park Conservation Laboratory, Chilton Foliat, Nr Hungerford, Berks
ROBSON, Mr. M.A.	Dept. of Conservation, Birmingham Museum & Art Gallery, Chamberlain Square, Birmingham B3 3DH
ROGERS, Mr. J.	Brighton
RYAN, Miss R.A.	British Museum, London
SADLER, Mr. J.D.	Ipswich Museum, High St., Ipswich, Suffolk
SCHWEIZER, Mr. F.	Laboratoire du Musee d'Art et d'Histoire, Geneva
SHEARMAN, Miss F.N.	British Museum, London
SLATE, Dr. P.M.B.	Ministry of Defence (PE), Quality Assurance Directorate, (Ordnance), Training Centre, Building 43, Royal Arsenal, West Woolwich SE18
SMITH, Mr. P.W.	Museum of Archaeology and Anthropology, Downing St., Cambridge CB2 3DZ
SMITH, Mr. R.D.	New Armouries, HM Tower of London, London EC3
SQUIRRELL, Miss J.P.	National Maritime Museum, Greenwich, London
STEVENS, Miss D.	National Maritime Museum, Greenwich, London
STIMSON, Mr. A	National Maritime Museum, Greenwich, London
SWEETNAM, Miss J.	Dept. of Maritime History, Merseyside County Museums, William Brown Street, Liverpool L3 8EN
THOMAS, Ms. S.A.	Herbert Art Gallery & Museum, Jordan Well, Coventry
TURGOOSE, Dr. S.	University College, Cardiff
TURNER, Mr. K.M.	Victoria & Albert Museum, London
TURNER, Mr. S.J.	Norwich Castle Museum, Norwich NR1 3JU
VAN GEERSDAELE, Mr. P.C.	National Maritime Museum, Greenwich, London
VARRALL, Mr. R.	National Maritime Museum, Greenwich, London

VINT, Miss J.	Lincoln Archaeological Trust
WALKER, Dr. R.	Dept. of Metallurgy & Materials Technology, University of Surrey, Guildford, Surrey GU2 6XH
WARD, Miss C.E.	Institute of Archaeology, London
WARD, Mr. D.A.	Rotherham Museum & Art Gallery, Clifton Park, Rotherham, South Yorks
WARD, Mr. M.J.	The Bass Museum, Horninglow St., Burton on Trent, Staffs
WARD, Miss S.E.	British Museum, London
WARDLEY, Miss K.V.	Castle Museum, Norwich
WATKINSON, Mr. D.	University College, Cardiff
WEBSTER, Mrs. K.L.	Kent County Museums Service, West Malling Air Station, Kent
WESTERN, Ms. A.C.	Dept. of Antiquities, Ashmolean Museum, University of Oxford, Beaumont St., Oxon
WHITE, Mr. R.	Lincoln Archaeological Trust
WILKS, Miss H.K.	Crafts Council, (Conservation Section), 8 Waterloo Place, London SW1Y 4AT
WILLIAMS, Miss J.S.H.	Conservation Dept., City of Birmingham Museum
WINSOR, Mr. P.R.	British Museum, London
WISE, Mrs. F.	National Maritime Museum, Greenwich, London
WOODWARD, Miss R.P.	Institute of Nautical Archaeology, PK 41, Bodrum, Turkey.

National Maritime Museum

MARITIME MONOGRAPHS AND REPORTS

Copies of these may be obtained from The Bookshop, National Maritime Museum, London SE10 9NF.

NATIONAL MARITIME MUSEUM SYMPOSIA ON ASPECTS OF MARITIME HISTORY

It is the Museum's intention to continue and extend its programme of symposia. Anyone interested in attending future meetings of this sort is invited to write to the Conference Officer, National Maritime Museum, London SE10 9NF, and ask for a copy of the programme.